CITY GARDENS

CITY GARDENS

An Open Spaces Survey in the City of London

Brian Plummer and Don Shewan
(City of London Polytechnic)

Belhaven Press
London and New York

CORPORATION
OF LONDON

First published in Great Britain in 1992 by
Belhaven Press (a division of Pinter Publishers),
25 Floral Street, London WC2E 9DS

British Library Cataloguing in Publication Data
A CIP catalogue record for this book is available from
the British Library

ISBN 1–85293–219–8

Library of Congress Cataloging-in-Publication Data
A CIP catalog record for this book is available from the Library of Congress

Typeset by City Cartographic and Desk Top Publishing Unit,
City of London Polytechnic, London E1 7NT

Printed in Great Britain by Bath Press Colourbooks, Glasgow

In memory of my parents
Mabel and Sydney Plummer.
B.P.

To my family.
D.S.

The Corporation of London is the local authority for the financial and commercial heart of Britain, the City of London. It is committed to maintaining and enhancing the status of the Business City as one of the world's three leading financial centres through the policies it persues and the high standard of services it provides. Its responsibilities extend far beyond the City boundaries and it provides a host of additional facilities for the benefit of the nation. These range from the Central Criminal Court, the Old Bailey, to the famous Barbican Arts Centre and open spaces such as Epping Forest and Hampstead Heath.

Among local authorities the Corporation is unique: not only is it the oldest in the country, combining its ancient traditions and ceremonial functions with the role of a modern and efficient authority, but it operates on a non-party political basis through its Lord Mayor, Aldermen and Members of the Court of Common Council.

The Corporation of London: a unique authority for a unique City.

Contents

Photographs

Figures

Tables

Foreword

 BUCKINGHAM PALACE.

Brian Plummer, Don Shewan and their colleagues have made a most valuable contribution to the long history of the City of London. This comprehensive survey of the open spaces in the City is interesting enough for contemporary readers, but it will become progressively more fascinating as the years roll by. I hope it will also draw attention to the social and aesthetic value of these open spaces and in so doing to protect them for the benefit of future generations. It may even encourage planners, developers, architects and engineers to add new spaces as they continue the process of bringing change to the City.

1991

Preface

Recurring public and political debate, together with a growing, and increasingly wide ranging professional interest and concern, has characterized discussion on the present and potential role of trees and open spaces within cities in the last decade. During this same period those charged with administering trees and gardens within cities have found themselves working in a more market oriented environment which demands greater value for money spent and justification in terms of benefits provided.

Any audit of open space within a city must commence with an inventory survey and evaluation. This exercise was undertaken within the City of London in 1982/3 by the Conservation class of the City of London Polytechnic joined by students from the Polytechnic of Central London and the University of Guelph, Canada.

The initial survey was carried out as a student practical exercise in which various facets of urban conservation and ecology were systemmatically recorded. The exercise built upon earlier experience gained in surveying squares in central London. Its objective, apart from encouraging students to look closely at the urban landscape on their own doorstep, was to provide as complete as possible an inventory of the nature and characteristics of these city green spaces together with a recording of all the City's street trees. Students were assigned individual areas and their results were combined onto master sheets to show the location and characteristics of all sites recorded. From the combined class results students were asked to present a digest of the results in various forms, highlighting any interesting observations, trends or patterns. Finally, students were asked to make an assessment of the 'value' of the City's open spaces from a number of different perspectives. At the conclusion of the course the two lecturers involved produced an eight page booklet summarising the results obtained. Any survey of this nature is subject to error and therefore in 1984/5 a verification survey was undertaken and corrections incorporated. Minor revisions to the original data have been made since.

Later additional surveys were also made in selected areas of the City to emphasize the functions open spaces fulfil in urban areas. The architectural contribution of open spaces and trees to the City's townscape; their individuality and character touched frequently with a nuance of countryside, park and garden. The recreational role of City spaces is extremely important, even in winter, to commuters and visitors. Their contribution as areas of rest and recreation has been examined in detail while the more discerning visitor may follow two City green trails which have been created to illustrate the infinite variety and interest of City gardens.

City open spaces, and more particularly trees and green spaces, provide habitats for other forms of wildlife, especially birds, and this function has been investigated in detail with particular reference to two City green spaces.

The contribution green spaces make to the improvement of the City's environment and, therefore, quality of life, has been investigated through surveys which illustrate the mitigating effects of green areas and trees to aural, visual and air pollution.

Open spaces, particularly green open spaces, together with street trees, form a valuable City resource and a considerable asset to the human population who live or work in or visit the City and some attempt has been made to assess this in financial terms.

The City is in a constant state of change, one measure of its vitality, but this has meant, inevitably, change to open spaces. Some major differences between the verification survey of 1984/5 and the situation today have been accounted for but some minor discrepancies may be noticeable to the discerning eye between the original verified pattern and that observed today.

Acknowledgements

The writing of a book of this nature is necessarily a co-operative effort and I would like to thank the many people who have laboured over parts of it. The book has greatly benefited from their diverse talents.

Its production has centred around the Geography Department of the City of London Polytechnic, which despite all the changes in recent years, remains a friendly helpful place in which to work,

My special thanks go to Don Shewan, manager of City Cartographic and DTP Unit and Superintendent in the Geography department. As graphics author of this book his conceptualisation of seemingly dull statistical material and his presentation of the photographic record have greatly enhanced the work.

Without the editorial and indexing skills of my friend and colleague in Conservation teaching, Mary Burgis, who literally took the manuscript by the horns, the present volume would have been immeasurably poorer. Several former students have contributed to this book and my thanks go particularly to John Slaughter for his work on chapter 8 and for his constant advice and support; to Jeremy Chapman for his willing work on the City Trails and the early draft of chapter 9; to Francis Williams for her contribution to chapter 6; and finally to Michael Walker for drawing many of the threads together.

It is always pleasant to acknowledge valued work from friends and former students who assisted with the surveys and some of the preliminary work on the book: M. Burbridge, J. Clarke, M. Clarke, A. Drumm, T. de Kaiser, G. Loemann, I. Mather, M. Newsam and C. Scales.

Typesetting, layout and design was prepared to their usual high standard by Andrew Ellis, Gareth Owen and Don Shewan of the Geography Department and the City Cartographic and DTP Unit at the City of London Polytechnic. The authors also wish to thank Gareth Owen for the preparation of all the final illustrations. Further illustrative help in earlier surveys and exhibitions was given by: J. Archer, J. Evans, C. Flewitt, E. Oliver and M. Teed. The original manuscript was word processed by Susan Shewan.

For the photographic record my thanks are particularly due to Hugh Lacey and John Slaughter. Other photographs were supplied by G. Coston, J. Langmead, P. Morris, Don Shewan and Brian Plummer.

A unique debt of gratitude goes to the Corporation of London the local authority for in the City of London and especially to those members and officers of the Corporation who, since the inception of this project, have facilitated and sustained our work over a number of years, and we are indebted to the Corporation for their financial support in making this publication possible.

My particular thanks are due to Miss Kate Williamson, Principal Planning Officer for the Department of Planning, who was the first person I approached and who favoured our proposals and pointed me in the right directions. My thanks go to Mr Peter Stagg, formally Superintendent of Parks and Gardens, for his invaluable help and guidance. At his suggestion to Members of the Trees, Gardens and City Open Spaces Committee we were invited to prepare an exhibit for the Corporation's Annual Flower Show at the Guildhall. Subsequently, year by year we have been delighted to accept an invitation to exhibit some of the Survey's highlights and updates at this show. Without the active interest and support of the sometime Chairman of the Planning and Communications Committee, Dr Keith Gugan, at an earlier stage it is most unlikely that the project would have prospered. Finally, my sincere thanks and gratitude are due to Mr David Jones, the present Superintendent of Parks and Gardens, who has constantly supported our work and pursuaded the Corporation to fund the publication of this fully illustrated book setting out and discussing the results of the Surveys in the context of an increasing awareness of the value of trees and open spaces within the City of London.

Lastly, my thanks are due to many people who have supplied information to us and to the working public of the City of London who have been such willing interviewees.

Brian Plummer
City of London Polytechnic

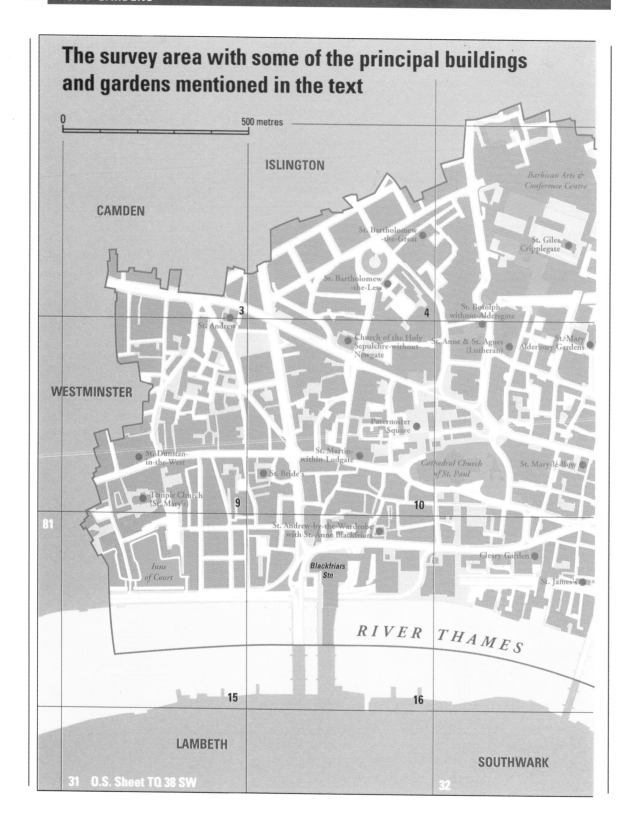

The survey area with some of the principal buildings and gardens mentioned in the text

0 500 metres

ISLINGTON

CAMDEN

Barbican Arts & Conference Centre

St. Bartholomew -the-Great

St. Giles Cripplegate

St. Bartholomew -the-Less

3

4

St. Botolph- without-Aldersgate

St. Andrew's

Church of the Holy Sepulchre-without Newgate

St. Anne & St. Agnes (Lutheran)

St. Mary Alderbury Gardens

WESTMINSTER

Paternoster Square

St. Dunstan- in-the-West

St. Martin- within-Ludgate

Cathedral Church of St. Paul

St. Mary-le-Bow

St. Bride's

Temple Church (St. Mary's)

9

10

St. Andrew-by-the-Wardrobe with St. Anne Blackfriars

81

Inns of Court

Blackfriars Stn

Cleary Garden

St. James's

RIVER THAMES

15

16

LAMBETH

SOUTHWARK

32

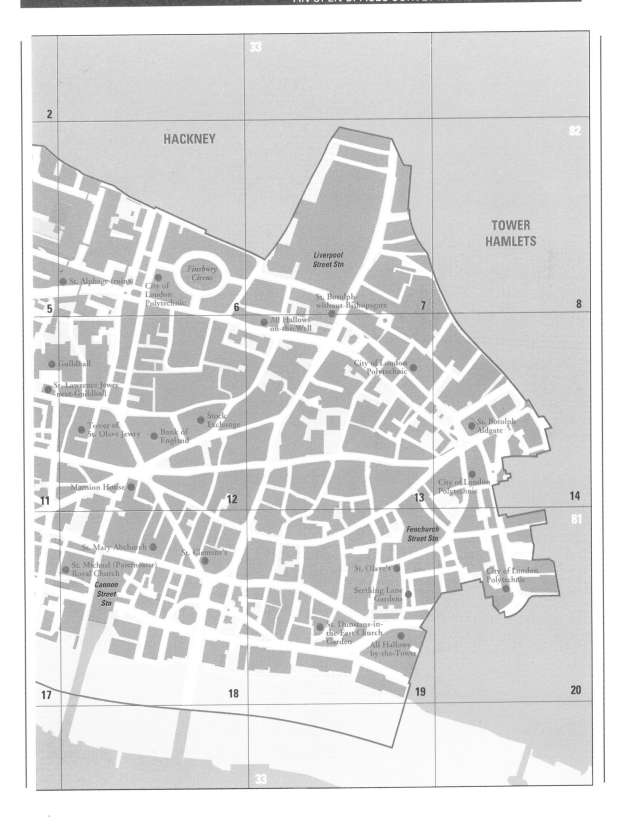

Holborn Circus a City Garden

CHAPTER 1

Introduction

From Babylonian times city gardens have been associated with paradise and expressed eclectically through human history. In the western world there was a particular flowering in the eighteenth century. At this time paradise was equated with the Arcadian ideal and recorded by many famous writers and painters. In the more prosaic age which followed, many gardens, tinged by the Romantic movement, became veritable oases, in many, none too pleasant, nineteenth century cities providing the only fleeting glimpse of paradise some poor citizens saw.

Today the City of London gardens offer commuters and visitors, albeit briefly and often unwittingly, a refuge, a retreat for conviviality or peace in the garden of the mind – our late twentieth century paradise.

Some of the qualities which perpetuate the attractiveness of gardens and endow them with an emotional as well as natural wealth are explored below.

Nature in Cities

It is evident from any perusal of architectural and planning literature that nature has always played an important role in cities. Although its function may have changed it is no less true today than in former times.

Nature in cities, especially in central areas, is most obvious in the form of street trees and small planted spaces frequently with grassed patches, flower beds, shrubberies and trees. Many open spaces are hard surfaced but here too trees, shrubs and flowers are often to be found in beds, tubs and planters. As might be expected birds are the most widely noticed urban fauna. Many open spaces, particularly those with shrubs, provide potential shelter and nest sites; more importantly perhaps, they provide a source of food primarily from humans and occasionally from plants and associated insect species.

Human Need

The need for nature in cities is frequently questioned. Indeed, in the City of London where the price of land and associated rent is so high it might be thought quite logical to suggest a progressive exclusion of nature from the financial heartland of the nation. How then can we justify the need? Put most simplistically, in cities, no less than in the countryside, we are still anatomically and physiologically mammals dependent, albeit now at several removes, on nature for an existence (Hackett 1983). Equally important for our fulfilment are the spiritual, emotional and psychological elements of nature in underlining this symbiosis. More and more, man will need the deep influence of nature to balance the effects of life in the modern city or, more prosaically, relief from central area pressures.

This underlying need for the sustaining caress of nature is not easily explained but has to do with the relationship indicated above. Vegetation, particularly trees and flowers in the city, are rich symbols of life mirroring the transitory changes and uncertainties as a kaleidoscope of colour and shadow and of sound and movement while the lasting beauties are seen as the seasons succeed one another, from seed time, planting and growing in spring onward, through flowering and fruitfulness in summer and autumn, to leaf-fall and decay in winter, tinged with the evident promise of renewal. A city's plants provide an eloquent reminder of the inescapable cycle of which we ourselves are part and in some way explain the strangely immeasurable but unchanging role of nature in fulfilling our deeper needs. The need for nature shows itself as an urge for contact with other forms of life besides our own (Manning 1979).

Nature exercises a profound influence on all of us in our everyday lives whether it is consciously articulated or not, whether we experience it frequently or in fleeting moments. The evidence for this is not hard to find and expresses itself in many forms – indoor plants in company entrances and offices, atriums, conservatories, window boxes, hanging gardens and climbing plants, countless trees and, of course, the conventional green spaces themselves. These 'nature' spaces are often perceived of as green oases surrounded by stark city buildings – an association heightened when these 'oases' are seen as places of relaxation and contemplation and spiritual enrichment separated from the surrounding places of work.

Aesthetics

It is clear that many elements of nature in cities satisfy deep-seated needs and wishes of people who live there or who come to work and visit. It is difficult to quantify this satisfaction although we suspect that nearly everyone would be unhappy if nature were to be totally excluded from our cities (see Youngman 1979). We suspect that a large part of the appeal of trees, flowers and other plants or small open spaces, apart from the symbolic and emotional appeal discussed above and the convenience of such spaces for sitting and resting, lies in aesthetic attractiveness, that is, their visual beauty.

It is often said that 'beauty is in the eye of the beholder'; certainly it is a matter of individual preference which itself will be influenced by our personal background, attitudes and outlook on life (Manning 1979). Furthermore, visual preferences change from generation

to generation. Over the last twenty years there has been a remarkable growth of interest in nature which has heightened our visual awareness and appreciation of the trees and green spaces around us in cities. Changing social attitudes and more leisure time have also influenced the design of green spaces within cities towards providing usable floorscape, permitting ease of access and a generally more 'open' plan to aid circulation and recreation. These and other developments all have a distinct influence on the visual appearance of these spaces.

The aesthetic attraction of trees and open spaces within cities lies in a number of landscape design and historical attributes, frequently working together, which may be summarised as

- introducing a sense of human scale and proportion

- mitigating the visual poverty of many buildings

- introducing a rural element as a foil to the surrounding townscape and

- in many instances, forming a quintessential part of the character of a city.

Perhaps one of the most important visual attributes of vegetation in cities, especially trees, lies in its ability to give a congruity of scale and proportion to many streets and spaces: by reducing the inhuman bulk of some buildings, increasing the scale of narrow streets and small courtyards (see Fairbrother 1974), and extending our impression of greenery 'beyond' by effectively diffusing our view.

At a very basic level trees and plants can disguise, or screen off, some of the less desirable townscape elements such as back and end walls or out-of-place additions to buildings. Some bland modern buildings can be visually enhanced by the filigreed or sculptural qualities of different foliage outlined against walls, by providing colour contrast or by changing shadows in winter.

The aesthetic value of trees and green spaces may also

be expressed in terms of their rural impact – how much they create an illusion of countryside and natural amenity in the urban environment (see Burman and Lloyd 1979). The visual appeal of *rus in urbe* cannot be underestimated. Perhaps the most important aesthetic attraction of trees and green places in urban areas is that they are there as of right, forming in landscape terms an essential part of the urban fabric, summarised in Pope's words 'consult the genius of place in all'. It is inconceivable to consider the Temple without its courts and gardens, St Paul's without the traditional green space of its churchyard, the Livery Companies without their 'secret gardens' (Boardman 1982), and All Hallows-on-the-Wall without its five trees.

Recreation

The City's green spaces provide not only for an inner contemplation and for an admiration of the natural beauty of plants and trees as they enhance the townscape, they also make a more commonplace contribution to our needs by providing outdoor areas for rest and relaxation. The extent to which green spaces, and open spaces generally, are used for this purpose depends on a number of factors.

Obviously the weather conditions and the time of year will play a crucial role; location (convenience) is perhaps the most important factor determining their use. Their design and layout, their facilities (seats) and the behaviour of other users are also important factors in determining the degree of use.

Generally open spaces in the City provide for what is termed passive activities such as walking, eating lunch, sitting, reading, observing, waiting and talking. Only a few open spaces in the City with public access provide entertainment such as lunchtime concerts or have facilities for active recreation such as tennis or bowls.

Practical problems arise from the recreational use of City green space. Some areas are carefully laid out but in such a way as to inhibit their recreational use, as if they were meant to be contemplated only from the periphery or viewed from inadequate pathways within. The result is often a lack of usable floorscape for the

public which results in 'competition' for the space available and possible 'conflict' between those moving through and those relaxing within the area at peak periods of use. This problem can be exacerbated where the green space has 'evolved' from other uses, for instance as a churchyard, and has not been designed specifically for public recreation.

This observation has wider implications, for instance it highlights differences of approach to greenspace management. Some would seek to emphasize the importance of natural beauty while others regard the primary function of green space as to provide maximum recreational opportunities.

Hard surfaces within green spaces are often frowned upon but it should be recognized, especially in spaces with heavy public use, that adequate provision of a durable surface is both practicable and desirable given our climate. Furthermore, with careful attention to design, and selection of materials, such surfaces can provide an effective floorspace, adding rather than detracting from the overall aesthetic effect.

Lack of available floorspace for recreation often results from a disproportionate area of the space being devoted to flower beds and shrubberies with trees, with a resulting inhibiting effect on the public use of such spaces. It is also evident from our investigation that too dense and, particularly, too complete a canopy in green spaces will produce a very shady environment, which, except for short summer periods, will have a depressing effect on people and limit their use. Sometimes this is further reinforced by the presence of behavioural deviants as well as unwelcome attention from birds.

Ecology

The ecological function (processes and relationships by which living and non-living things relate to one another) of trees and green space within city centres is generally less well perceived by the public although it contributes significantly to the overall quality of city life in a number of ways.

Over the last fifteen years there has been an enormous

growth of public interest in the natural world. This is evident from the estimated three million people who are members of conservation organisations, and from the high ratings of wildlife programmes on radio and television. One notable feature has been a growing interest in nature in cities which has taken many forms, from a study of existing urban ecosystems to the creation of artificial wildlife habitats and the 'naturalising' of parks and green areas.

The urban ecosystem may be best considered as a continuum, the central areas of a city being at one extreme while at the other are to be found remnant woods, commons and heaths. There is a gradation between these two extremes within which lies the completely man-made ecosystems – the anthropogenic biocenoses of Duvigneaud (1975) – planted trees and landscaped green spaces.

As there are many different attitudes towards nature in cities, it may be useful to ask what exactly we understand by 'nature'. Differing views can perhaps best be illustrated by considering nature in terms of a sociological continuum. At the one extreme there are those who opt for nature rampant and apparently in control, whereas at the other man is very definitely in charge of the difference between wilderness areas and carefully manicured gardens (see Manning 1979). Even in the urban environment both have their place but it is obvious that for many reasons such as stressed environments, particular patterns of use and cultural attitudes, we are at the man-dominated end of the spectrum in central city areas. However, it should not be assumed from this that the trees and green spaces within the City of London are ecologically unimportant.

The central districts of the City can hardly be described as a floral desert but rather as 'a built environment containing havens of natural life, not only plants but insects and birds' (Burman and Lloyd 1979). There are a number of ways in which this natural life enhances the environment.

Firstly, many City green spaces do possess reasonable vegetational diversity which results in a variety of habitats being present for wildlife. Secondly, those charged with the management of some open spaces have planted a great variety of species, particularly introduced and exotic, which are of interest and form miniature arboreta. There is a more practical side too, as many of these plants come from regions of far greater climatic extremes than our own and consequently have an inbuilt resistance to adverse aspects of the urban environment which is superior to many native species. Thirdly, vegetation, particularly trees and shrubs, ameliorate some harmful features associated with city environments.

Summary

Trees and green spaces are important elements in any built landscape. They fulfil a number of functions, summarised below, which taken together enhance the quality of life for those who live, work or visit cities.

- Contact points with nature which provide redress from the pressures of urban living and furnish an environment for personal enrichment.

- Trees and other plants, as living art forms, provide a sense of scale and balance and give visual pleasure which transforms and enhances our perception of a city's townscape.

- Many green areas provide usable space for everyday life and outdoor recreation (see Tregay 1984).

- Within the urban ecosystem the communities created by man provide many interesting and unusual habitats for insects, small mammals and birds, at the same time contributing environmental benefits.

CHAPTER 2

City of London Open Spaces in Perspective

Historical Perspective

The townscape of the City has been continually changing throughout London's history. These changes have been perhaps most evident since the Second World War, particularly in the last twenty years as new building techniques have facilitated a period of intense development. Many parts of the City that were destroyed in the Second World War have now been entirely redeveloped, sometimes on a 'massive' scale, such as is the case with the Barbican. Such changes will continue and "the City of the twenty-first century will be a very different place from the City of today" (Fisher 1976).

Centuries of building and rebuilding to meet the changing requirements of the City have resulted in many alterations, both in the area and the nature of open spaces in the square mile. Nevertheless, despite these changes, open spaces, particularly green spaces, are a vital element of the City's townscape today and there is every reason to suggest that they will remain so and continue to enhance the quality of the City environment in the future.

The evolution of present day patterns of open spaces in the City has been a continuous process; this chapter traces this evolution and examines the impact of the major changes that have shaped the City's open space heritage.

Open Space in Medieval Times

The beginnings of the present pattern of open spaces can be traced to the medieval period. A reconstruction of the layout of medieval London based on archaeo-logical evidence (Corporation of London 1978a) indicates a large number of churches, which would have presumably incorporated open spaces in the form of churchyards and burial grounds. Other areas of open space originating in this period were the Inner and Lower Temple gardens (Weinreb and Hibbert 1983), together with some early Livery Companies gardens. The oldest surviving Livery Company garden is that of the Worshipful Company of Merchant Taylors in Threadneedle Street, first recorded in 1415 (Cleary 1982), while the Worshipful Company of Girdlers have had a garden in Basinghall Street since the 15th century.

A considerable amount of unoccupied land lay towards the north and east of the City boundary (Corporation of London 1978a). On the present site of Smithfield Market, livestock trading, tournaments, sports and executions were held, together with the Bartholomew Fair, while on the present site of Gracechurch Street a corn and hay market was held. At this time the amount of usable open space in the City per head of population was probably greater than at any later period.

In addition to these public spaces, domestic gardens were common, varying in size according to locality. Within the centre of the city they were generally small enclosed plots, while towards the outskirts they were larger, adjoining houses set back from the street (Lloyd 1979); as early as 1175 Fleet Street had been described as a suburb with 'spacious gardens' (Lloyd 1979). Gardens were personal and protected havens in an insecure period of London's history and usually included a surrounding wall. During this period gardening became an increasing source of employment, reflected in the existence of the fraternity of the City

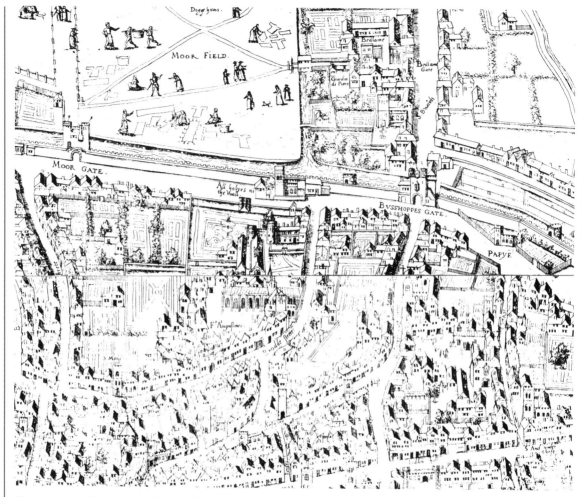

Figure 2.1   Copperplate Map (1553-9).

Guild of Gardeners in 1345 (Cleary 1982), the fore-runners of the present Worshipful Company of Gardeners. By Elizabethan times London was noted for its gardens; Stow (in Cleary 1982) writes that every house of any size had a 'fair garden plot', while Cleary (1982) writes that London must have been something of a garden city. Other spaces such as the Gardens of St Helen, stretching from Bishopsgate to St Mary Axe, and a number of spacious gardens lying outside the wall, such as the 'Giardin di Piero' (many of which now lie beneath the site of Liverpool Street Station) were important at this time, and can be seen on the Copperplate map (1553-9, Fig. 2.1), or the Agas map (c.1562).

Early Losses of Open Space

In the Tudor period dramatic changes occurred in both the area and ownership of open space. It has been estimated that the population of the City increased almost fourfold between 1530 and 1605, from 50,000 to 190,000 (Lloyd 1979); this resulted in pressure on open spaces in two ways – the use of vacant land for building, and the infilling of yards and domestic gardens so that development became denser. These changes were facilitated by the earlier dissolution of the monasteries, whereby much of the open space associated with the Church was transferred to private hands, much of it then being built on (Fisher 1976). An

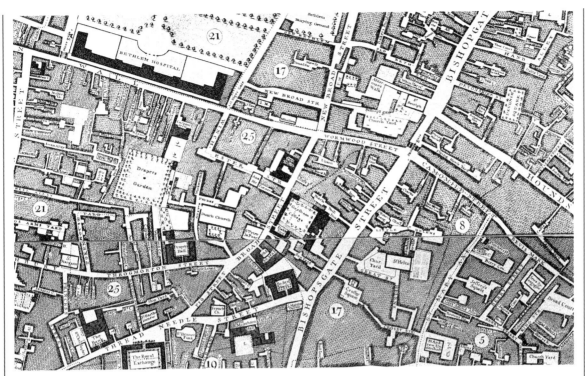

Figure 2.2   Rocque Map (1746).

example is the open space of Austin Friars: once the site of the orchards of Augustinian monks, it was reduced to a network of garden enclaves; some effects of the changes can be seen on the maps mentioned above.

The Great Fire and After

The Great Fire of 1666 destroyed all buildings within the City walls, except for an eastern section between the Tower and Bishopsgate, and some western areas along Fleet Street (Lloyd 1979). Although much of the City was reduced to 'open space', rebuilding began almost immediately, largely to the same pattern so that the opportunity to rebuild the City with landscaped public gardens was not realised. The gardens of the City still resembled a mosaic of small open spaces as indicated in John Ogilby's *Survey of the City* (1676). During reconstruction two major routes were built, King Street and Queen Street, but although a few minor modifications were made, the chance to build a newly planned City was put aside in favour of quick reconstruction along the lines of what had been there

before by the existing property owners (Lloyd 1979). With rebuilding came further growth, especially in the commercial sector, and a continuing decline of private domestic open space as the resident population declined. Many of the fields and open spaces of Tudor London were lost to rebuilding and redevelopment; for instance, the Rocque map (1746, Fig. 2.2) shows the loss of open space within the Austin Friars and St Helens Gardens areas. A continuation of this trend of increasing building density is illustrated on the Horwood map (1799, Fig. 2.3).

Influences Shaping Open Spaces in the Eighteenth Century

An aspect of the 18th century scientific and aesthetic 'enlightenment' was an increase in interest in the 'natural world'. Due to widening trade links the City was a focus for the introduction of many exotic species. Christopher Smart (1722-71) realised the potential of these exotics for London's gardens in praying to God to 'bless improvements in gardening till London be a

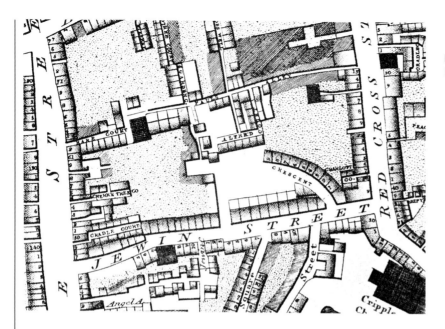

Figure 2.3
Horwood Map (1799).

City of palm trees'. Thomas Fairchild, in the *London Gardener* (1722) describes methods of growing evergreens, fruit trees, flowering shrubs and exotic plants, which he suggests could thrive well in London's gardens (Cleary 1982). A further aspect of this change was in the function of the City's remaining domestic gardens; rather than augmenting the City's food base, as they had done earlier, they now took on a more aesthetic role.

During the 17th and 18th centuries the design of gardens was greatly influenced by Italian and French formalism, having its roots in the Renaissance. Gardens, however small, focused on a central feature with paths leading from it at right angles. It was also at this period that open spaces were first designed for, and used solely as, areas for public recreation. Other open spaces were increasingly used for pleasure. Bowling had been popular since Elizabethan times and the walks of the Inns of Court were much patronised in Charles II's reign. However, the increasing density of the City's buildings meant that, with few exceptions, there was little chance for public open space development in the square mile, most of the remaining open spaces being associated with churches or the Livery Companies. By the end of the 18th century the movement of people out from the City was gathering

momentum, but the newly established developments in the West End still influenced residential development in and around the City; 'desirable residential developments for people of quality', laid around a communal green space in the style of some West End housing, were established just outside the City wall. Three formal developments in the City were influenced by such Georgian architectural design: Devonshire Square, a scheme to the west of Minories including a small circus, crescent and square laid out in 1767-70 of which a part, much restored, still remains; and the only remaining example of a fashionable Georgian open space, Finsbury Circus (1815). The Horwood map (Fig. 2.3) shows the initial stages of a crescent being built at Jewin Street, the completed formal layout can be seen on Wylds' map (1842, Fig. 2.4); this development no longer exists, it being on the site of the present-day Barbican complex.

Nineteenth and Twentieth Century Changes

From the mid-19th century to the outbreak of the Second World War changes continued both in the social and physical structure of the City, which were reflected in the nature and distribution of open space. By the mid-19th century the trend in increased building had led to a further separation of activities between the town and country and the inevitable loss of more City open space. City residents now travelled to surrounding fringe areas to enjoy the larger open spaces there (Lloyd 1979). Wroth (1896) describes City dwellers escaping the congestion of the City to visit the small 'rural resorts' of Islington, or Spring Gardens, Fox Hill (later Vauxhall Gardens).

Commercial building pressure within the City increased dramatically during the 19th and early 20th centuries. During the same period the residential population of the City declined from 128,000 in 1801 to only 9000 in 1939 (Lloyd 1979). There was, however, an increase in the City's daytime population from 170,000 in 1866 to 500,000 in 1935 (Corporation of London, 1944). These population changes reflect the increasing importance of business activity and a further loss of domestic open space as remaining domestic gardens were replaced by office buildings.

This pattern of continuing reduction in open space can be seen clearly in the case of Draper's Gardens, in fact the whole Austin Friars area epitomises these developments. On the Copperplate map (Fig. 2.1) it formed part of the gardens and orchard of the Austin Friars. By 1574 it had been sold to Thomas Cromwell, the Drapers acquiring it ten years later. The Rocque map (Fig. 2.2) shows that by 1746 it had diminished in size and was now surrounded by buildings. A further reduction in size and change of shape is recorded on Horwoods map (Fig. 2.3), and by 1842 (see Fig. 2.4) it had a much more formal appearance, with a centrepiece and tree and shrub borders. By the end of the last century the large garden had disappeared. The original gardens live on as a street name, and as a hard space with planters and a fountain centrepiece, surrounding a part of National Westminster Bank in Throgmorton Street (an elevated patio area is being reconstructed to increase the size of the split level hard space). The present private garden of the Drapers Company is a long narrow, smaller garden with trees, planters, pond and statue. This garden is situated along the lower part of Throgmorton Street between Austin Friars and the Drapers Hall, and provides a good example of how an open space may change sites while retaining the name.

Improvements in public transport during Victorian

times enabled the growing city workforce to move further away from work and into the suburbs. This process led to the loss of more open space as the transport infrastructure was constructed. For example, Wylds map (Fig. 2.4) shows reasonably large gardens in the Liverpool Street and Blomfield Street areas. Broad Street station was subsequently built here as the terminus for the North London Railway. As the number of open spaces declined, so the value of those remaining increased. Allinghams (1860) observed that 'a garden's a garden anywhere, but twice a garden in London' (Cleary 1982).

The loss of open space continued as City developers largely ignored their importance, their new buildings making little provision for amenity. However, it was recognised by some that the growing daytime workforce needed green spaces. Alexander McKenzie, in *The Parks, Open Spaces and Throughfares of London* (1869), regretted the lack of open space found in the heart of London, and compared it unfavourably with Paris where outdoor recreation was of great social importance. It was, however, the traditional City institutions that protected and maintained the existing green spaces. The Livery Companies were of major importance to green space management as the Victorian gardens of the Merchant Taylors, Grocers, Drapers and Salters illustrate. The latter part of the 19th century saw renewed interest in the creation, protection and maintenance of the City's open space. In 1882 the Metropolitan Public Gardens Association was formed and, working with the Corporation of London, public gardens were laid out.

The Impact of the Burial Legislation
and Other Developments

The City has a large number of churches within a small area; previously most of these had burial grounds. A series of Acts between 1855 and 1888 terminated burials in City churchyards while at the same time ensuring their continued existence as open spaces most of which were subsequently used for public enjoyment and are now maintained by the Corporation of London.

The 1855 Burial Act was used as an opportunity to develop, among others, St Botolph's Without

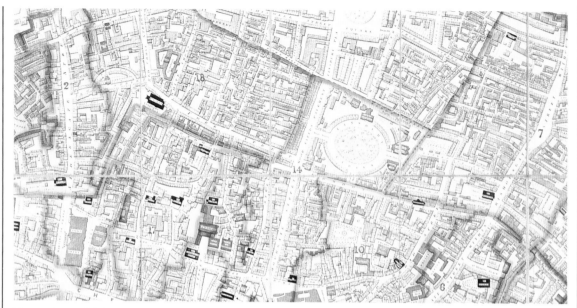

Figure 2.4   Wyld's Map (1842).

Bishopsgate churchyard as a garden, including seating, with the churchwardens being responsible for maintenance. Churchyards no longer used for burial, which were being used as public open space by the time of the 1875 Ordnance Survey, include St Helens Bishopsgate, St Giles Cripplegate, St Botolph's Aldgate, and All-Hallows-by-the-Tower. After the 1884 Disused Burial Grounds Act, more public gardens were developed from obsolete graveyards, and managed either by the Church or by the Corporation for the Church. A notable example is Postman's Park formed by the conversion of the disused burial ground of St Botolph's Without Aldersgate (1880), and the incorporation of the graveyards of Christchurch (1890), St Leonard Foster, and a strip of land fronting Little Britain (1900). This open space is one of the largest in the City and, although originally the responsibility of the parish, it is now maintained by the Corporation.

Many of the Victorian burial grounds exhibited similar characteristics, in that each had curved paths and were set out 'naturally' and were thus less formal than the gardens of the 17th and 18th centuries, indeed many of the City's open spaces still reflect this Victorian parkscape. The 1880 Disused Burial Ground Act gave these open spaces as much protection as possible: no

development was allowed except for religious purposes, and as the population had declined, the churches were under no great pressure to expand, so the spaces were really protected in perpetuity. This culmination of burial ground legislation showed the recognition and importance attached to the open spaces in the City, or of not building on your forefathers' graves.

At the same time as these Burial Acts were being used for the maintenance of open spaces, other green spaces in the City came under the Corporation's protection and management: Finsbury Circus was acquired for public use by an Act of Parliament in 1900; St Paul's Churchyard and Smithfield recreation ground also came under the protection of the Corporation at this time.

Although the larger of the late 19th century and early 20th century gardens were outside the core area of the City, the hub of the City (in the vicinity of the Bank and the Stock Exchange), where building density is highest, benefited from small public gardens laid out in churchyards. Examples include St Michael's, Cornhill, and the pleasant small tree-shaded churchyard of St Stephen Walbrook (Lloyd 1979).

Thus as the City progressed into the 20th century the future for open spaces looked secure, the Corporation had an extremely positive view towards open space (as seen in the creation and assimilation of open spaces), and also had the necessary legal power (under the Burial Grounds Acts) to protect this space for the future.

Reconstruction after the Second World War

We have already seen that after the Great Fire of 1666, the chance to re-plan the City was not taken up. The City had a second chance to re-plan after the bomb damage of the blitz of the Second World War. The devastation caused by the bombs created many 'open spaces', allowing more light, air, space and colour into the City than there had been for a long time. This opportunity for change coincided with the new planning ideologies of Howard and Abercrombie – that, as workers and inhabitants alike depended on green open spaces for relaxation and recreation, they were necessary and intrinsic components of a city's fabric. This was reflected in both strategic and local planning, both of which encouraged the provision of public open space. The County of London Plan (Forshaw and Abercrombie 1943) made recommendations for standard minimum open space requirements which were much higher than the existing levels for many London areas. The Corporation of London (1944), realised that they needed another 16 ha of open space in the City to come into line with Abercrombie's proposals, an amount of land that they did not have. The Corporation of London recognised the deficiency in open space but due to competing land uses were forced to 'hesitate to adopt any particular proportion (of land as open space), but recognise the desirability of securing the highest standards of amenity that circumstances may permit or that may appear desirable'. The report also noted the effect of open spaces as fire-breaks, and although no specific sites were mentioned, the Corporation were more committed to small intimate areas, thinking that large parks were effectively a barrier to communication between users. The Interim Report on Reconstruction in The City (Corporation of London, 1946) envisaged an open space system which would be capable of gradual addition and improvement, as visitors and office workers would be more likely to use a system

of connected open spaces as part of potential 'pedestrian circuits' including sites of City interest; for example, the report suggests a circuit via St Paul's Churchyard, St Vedast's, Goldsmiths Hall, Noble Street, London Wall and St Giles Cripplegate (see green trails, p.65). The subsequent redevelopment of many sites in the City has incorporated open spaces as a matter of deliberate planning policy. The Corporation's present policy is to resist the loss of existing open space unless adequate provision for replacement can be made (Corporation of London 1986).

The post-war phase of open space development has been the most important in the City's history as there has been an increase in the number and total area of green spaces. The green space survey indicates that the larger open spaces in the City (with the exceptions of Finsbury Circus and Temple Gardens) follow a broad band from the Barbican to St Paul's, an area shown on Bacon's Plan (c1946) to have suffered some of the heaviest bombing of the war. This illustrates the high degree of implementation of planning policies, with bomb-sites and wasteground being converted to open space, in direct contrast to the period after the Great Fire of 1666.

The Barbican complex houses the greatest concentration of post-war open spaces in the City. The Barbican plan involved a mainly residential complex of high density development, with the provision of as much open space as possible. Thus 3.2 ha of the 14 ha site has been set aside for the creation of a variety of open spaces, from formal public 'hard' space to intimate domestic gardens. Private communal gardens such as those at Wallside accompany a small scale return to domestic gardens in the City such as those at Andrewes House (see green trail). Both types of space are important, and both can be enjoyed by visitors or passersby. Within the open spaces of the Barbican many varieties of trees, shrubs and flowers have been planted which add an element of rurality to such areas as the Defoe or Fann Street Gardens. Apart from green spaces, the 'Hanging Gardens' visually soften the bold architectural lines of the Barbican buildings. The feeling of rurality and seclusion is heightened in the Barbican open spaces as they are generally enclosed by buildings which act as buffers to the surrounding noise of the

City. Within the complex are the gardens of St Alphage and the Salters which have been planted and landscaped to fit in well with the exposed section of Roman wall. Similarly the churchyard of St Giles Cripplegate has been treated as part of the new development and is surrounded by a brick pavement (see green trail).

The City has seen an increase in hard space since the Second World War of which the St Giles Piazza is only one example. Another is Paternoster Square to the north of the Cathedral, which is a large stark pedestrian precinct flanked by offices and shops, and the open area to the south-east, once the site of buildings, incorporates a considerable area of open space which has been treated in an unimaginative way (Freeman 1979).

A number of churchyards have also been developed as a result of war damage, St Olave's is a carefully maintained green space which contains a fine oak tree, while the churchyard of St Anne and St Agnes has been extended on its eastern side due to bomb damage. The site of the church and churchyard of St Mary's Aldermanbury has been well-treated; the church was destroyed in the war and its ruins were removed for re-creation at Fulton, Missouri (France 1979). The site is developed on two levels (see green trail), the foundations being left as an integral design feature among the lawns and trees, so that the area provides ideal seclusion from the noisy surroundings. Another church largely destroyed in the war, St Dunstan's in the East, has been developed into the largest garden created by the Corporation of London this century (Cleary 1982). The ruined walls have been retained and incorporated into a garden 'which skillfully combines architectural elements with greenery' (Freeman 1979). Recently plans have been put forward for the redevelopment of this area involving a ground level pattern of pedestrian walkways, which avoid the present severe grid layout, separating individual buildings designed more sympathetically in style and orientation and grouped loosely around a central hard open space.

Three other notable gardens have been created by the Corporation since the war, all on bomb-damaged land. The 1951 Festival Gardens and the Information Centre Gardens next to St Paul's Churchyard follow the ground plan of the pre-war buildings on whose ruins they were laid out. They now provide a formal garden setting as a backdrop to St Paul's and 'open up' the Cathedral, in contrast to the closely knit development characterising this area before the war. The churchyard has also been enlarged to include a wide variety of trees, shrubs and flowers. The Cleary Garden in Queen Victoria Street is another post-war multi-level development laid out to celebrate the centenary of the Metropolitan Public Gardens Association. There is a smaller formal green area at Aldermanbury Square which forms a focal point to the surrounding buildings, while the nearby Noble Street Gardens, as well as revealing sections of the City wall, contained a section of 'wild garden' until recently removed.

The gardens of the Livery Companies, although not technically 'new' open spaces, have changed much since the war. Some have been started anew, for example the Salters' Garden, while some have expanded, taking in pieces of bomb-damaged land, for example the Goldsmiths' Garden, which has incorporated the churchyard of St John Zachary in Gresham Street.

Churchyards are still important in providing a source of City open space, especially in those parts of the City where other types of open space are rare. Although the Churchyards of St Botolph's Bishopsgate, St Helen's Bishopsgate and other older open spaces may seem small in comparison to some of the new formal gardens, their importance as green areas in the crowded City has not been diminished.

The high density of development in the City and the ever-changing townscape means that land that is unused does not remain so for long. The west end of Ludgate Hill represents the final site in the City to be developed after the destruction of the Second World War. It has involved the removal of the rail bridge across Ludgate Hill, the construction of a new City Thameslink station and office infill. Until recently the area had been used as a car park which was surrounded by vestiges of wasteland colonisers with such plants as the wall rocket, michaelmas daisy, evening primrose and buddleia (Greater London Ecology Unit 1986).

The last two decades have seen the 'greenscaping' of

many of the City's routeways both pedestrian and vehicular. Street gardens form an element of many wider pavements. Some of these gardens act as a baffle between pedestrian and vehicular traffic for short distances while most form very pleasant visual features. City 'roadscapes' have been considerably enhanced by 'traffic gardens', those at Blackfriars being most spectacular; many others exist as linear features on roundabouts (for example, Moorgate) and are equally worthwhile as parts of the City's green architecture.

*   *   *   *   *

The City has retained its importance as a centre for world trade and finance, and is a place of work for some 300,000 people (Corporation of London 1986). During its history the City has experienced continuous pressure for development and redevelopment. Other pressures on the quality of life come from increased motor traffic and noise pollution; this means that relatively peaceful green enclaves of the City have increased in importance and will continue to do so. Present open spaces in the City must not be lost to re-development pressures lest the City be deprived of an integral part of its heritage.

This brief historical summary of the open spaces has shown that, although their evolution has been a continuous process, it has been shaped by notable events in the City's history which have changed the character, size and distribution of these spaces. In the last one hundred years the growing interest of the Corporation of London has led to more careful planning and protection of open spaces which hopefully will continue in the future.

Geographical Perspective

A number of models have been devised to explain land use patterns within cities. The idea of concentric zones illustrating the changes of land use which occur, associated with changes in a city's function as distance from the centre varies, is well known and features in many of London's planning exercises. Other approaches have emphasised the importance of directional factors, such as lines of communication, in segregating different land uses and thus dividing successive concentric zones

into a number of sectors or wedges. Yet another approach suggests the importance of a number of independent city growth points, as nuclei in explaining the evolution of the complex pattern of city land use we see today. Further ideas have been developed which stress the importance of economic and activity systems approaches (Carter 1981). All of these ideas are directed towards establishing a conceptual framework which will explain present land use patterns with a reasonable degree of verisimilitude.

These models not only provide some explanations for the overall pattern of land use in London but are equally useful in expressing the spatial distribution of a particular land use; therefore we can very briefly review the overall pattern of open space distribution in London in this context.

Distance from the Centre

The further we proceed outward from a city centre the greater will be the extent and variety of open space. In the case of London we can summarise the situation by considering five concentric zones of increasing distance from the centre of the city.

The innermost circle coincides with the central core of the City (Corporation of London, 1984). Within this zone open space forms a very small percentage of the total land area and comprises courtyards, generally small precincts, street planters and other small areas such as churchyards. Biogeographically, all these areas form completely artificial ecosystems.

The second zone surrounds the City core and extends outwards to embrace what is commonly called central London. For a number of limited reasons the liquidity pattern is slightly less dense and correspondingly open space occupies a somewhat greater area and there are more street trees. The spaces themselves show more variety in form. The ecosystems remain completely artificial and man-managed, but exhibit a greater degree of biological diversity than is the case within the core. It should be noted that within both these linear zones 'hard' spaces – when most of the 'floor' surface is made of hard materials as distinct from grass, flower beds and shrubberies – occupy a considerable proportion of the total open space.

In the two succeeding zones open space is of considerably greater importance both in terms of variety and extent and also in its biological diversity. The main elements are firstly parks, recreation and sports grounds, other landscaped areas such as hospital or school grounds, and metropolitan open land; and secondly, suburban domestic gardens. The ecosystems are still artificial but show a greater variety of fauna from a few areas with quasi natural and fairly rich communities to the more prevalent and biologically impoverished 'barren grassland'. Generally as distance increases from the centre individual areas of open space, especially domestic gardens, increase in size and the overall extent of open space increases as a percentage of the total land area.

Open space in the outermost zone includes those elements which have been recorded in the two previous zones within which the individual units generally occupy a great area. However, one of the most significant features in this outer zone is the remnants or 'islands' of semi-natural ecosystems, especially small patches of woodland.

Direction from the Centre

In a general way, successive concentric zones suggest the importance of distance from the city centre in explaining the extent and nature of open space distribution. However, direction is also important in refining the picture by means of an 'overlay' of sectors which emphasize a degree of separation of land uses which are particularly associated with the major lines of communication both out from the centre and peripherally. These sectors or corridors have more recently become particularly important in terms of London's open space. Two examples may be cited and others noted.

The best known corridor outwards from the centre is found by the Lea Valley, which today forms a very important 'open space sector' from the Thames to Enfield. It comprises the Lea Valley Regional Park together with the Hackney Marshes, Victoria Park and Mile End Park (GLC Strategic Park). The sector

provides a distinctive belt of recreational park land, sports fields, local nature reserves and other open space. It also incorporates a number of 'new' habitats which are developing on derelict industrial sites and other vacant areas located along this axis of communication (Goode 1983). A similar, though more discontinuous, and informally organized, sector can be recognized as being coincident with the main communication corridor westward from central London – a belated recognition of Abercrombie's 1943-4 proposals for bringing green lands to central London. As well as recreational land and sports fields it comprises artificial sites particularly rich in flora and fauna such as the Gunnersbury Triangle (Goode 1983) which are developing on vacant or derelict land. A more recent phenomenon associated with this axis of communication is the open space of the motorway verges which is of some biological interest. Other directional axes which provide a significant open space sector are the Roding Valley, Dagenham Corridor and the north-south wedge of the Colne Valley with its regional park on London's western periphery.

Independent Nuclei

Further significant differences in the extent and nature of open space occur towards the outer limits of the central zone and within the adjacent 'inner suburban' zone. These are largely unrelated to distance or directional influences and may be attributed to 'independent' factors. For instance, the considerable area of royal parkland immediately to the west of the central London zone can be traced to the fact that these areas formed a part of the Sovereign's hunting woods or grounds of royal palaces with the later and not unrelated addition of the Zoological and Botanical Gardens. In the City of Westminster open space accounts for some 25% of the total land area. During the 18th and 19th centuries the cities of London and Westminster, originating as independent nuclei, gradually merged. In this area, much sought after by business and government personnel, an extensive and distinctive pattern of green space developed, consisting of a mosaic of squares, crescents and gardens. The result is a considerable area of green space, often relatively rich in flora and fauna and visually attractive and quite dissimilar with the character of green space more generally associated with the central inner suburban zone at a similar distance from the city centre.

Summary

- This outline of the nature and distribution of London's open spaces shows the pattern to be far from simple. There is a great range in the types of open space to be observed, in their extent and in biogeographical contrasts.

- It has been shown that increasing distance from the centre of the city does not necessarily mean richer 'natural' open space environments. There are many enclosures in the form of gardens, reserves, new naturally developing communities, interesting exotic plantings and small but biologically diverse gardens to be found within the inner area of the city.

- The City of London open spaces, particularly green spaces, are especially important insofar as they represent a very small percentage of the total City area and as such are a scarce resource. This is largely explained by the fact that domestic gardens are almost non-existent in the City in comparison with the considerable areas occupied by this type of open space outside the core and central zones.

- Although within the City green spaces are represented completely by artificial ecosystems, many, through deliberate management policy, exhibit considerable vegetational diversity while at the same time representing natural life in an otherwise wholly urban environment.

Green Space Survey exhibition in the Guildhall

CHAPTER 3

The Surveys

The basic green space survey is presented here together with a brief outline of the way in which it was carried out. More detailed work has been added to the original survey to evaluate the importance of specific aspects of the City's green spaces such as their value to commuters and tourists, as a baffle to pollution, their aesthetic contribution to the City's architectural fabric and indeed their 'economic' value to the City and its community.

Survey Method

The City-wide Survey

The 1:10500 Ordnance Survey Sheets covering the City area provided the Survey Base Map. The NW, NE, SW and SE quadrants of these map sheets were numbered as squares 2-20 for the purposes of the Survey (see map p.xxiv). For each square street trees were plotted directly onto the map squares.

Open spaces were then categorized as hard (with a predominantly hard floorscape), green (with a predominantly soft floorscape: grass, flower beds, shrubberies, and so on) and street gardens (predominantly small planted linear areas forming an integral part of the City's pavement features and including areas planted to divide traffic flows, pedestrian or vehicular). Every open space in these three categories, within each square, was plotted on the base map and for each open space its features were recorded on site using an inventory sheet (Table 3.1).

A composite data sheet was then compiled for each square from the individual inventory sheets. The following calculations were then made for each open space category; number of spaces, total area, average area, standard deviation and size range. For hard spaces and green spaces the mean 'aesthetic rating' was calculated (see item 12, Table 3.1). A 'rurality index' was then devised (Table 3.2) by attributing 'rural' scores to items 4, 5, 6 and 9 from the Survey Inventory Sheet.

Special Surveys

In addition to the initial City-wide surveys this report is based on the results of several smaller but complementary surveys which are directed towards a better understanding of the natural, architectural and recreational uses and value of these open spaces to the City. These surveys' methods and results are more appropriately discussed in the relevant sections of this report although some general points should be made here.

These special surveys fall into three categories: they may be based on or combined with survey data derived from the initial City-wide surveys; they may compare and contrast this survey data with other reports and published material; or again they may represent new survey material.

Taking the first category, this includes the vegetational diversity survey; the architectural and overall value of street trees derive most of their data from the initial surveys. The City green trails also involved the use of initial vegetation and aesthetic data to determine a 'pleasantness' value for each site; the attractiveness and transient invocation of a 'rural' quality within the City – *rus in urbe* – has been calculated as a 'rurality' index.

Table 3.1 The inventory of data recorded for each open space during the baseline survey of the City of London

1	Type of area	(hard, green, street garden)
2	Access to public open/closed	
3	Area of vegetation (m²)	(only applicable to open spaces)
4	Percentage of area vegetated	(only applicable to green spaces)
5	Structure of vegetation: G, F, S, T	(grass, flowerbeds, shrubberies, trees)
6	Number of trees	
7	Age of trees: S, Y, M, O	(recently planted, young, mature, senile)
8	Species of trees	
9	Bird species seen	(note any evidence of vegetation being used for feeding or nesting)
10	Number of people	(enter time and number of people seen in area)
11	Activities observed	(indicate activities in area; walking through, sitting, eating, reading, other (specify) "meths" drinking (include where there is supportive evidence *i.e.* bottles)
12	Design and aesthetic rating	(enter subjective score for each of the following attributes on a rating of 1–5)

Attributes	Subjective Score 1–5	Mean
a Urban	Rural	
b Incongrous	Harmonious	
c Noisy	Calm	
d Littered	Tidy	
e Dull	Attractive	

Notes for scoring

a The rural illusion is heightened by: shadows, shades, colours, soft textured surfaces, birdsong, plants; individually and as a "screen" from surrounding buildings and road space.

b Harmonious and pleasing design entails a well-proportioned layout in the space with due regard to the nature of the surrounding buildings, avoiding emptiness on the one hand and cluttered horticultural or municipal "bric-a-brac" on the other.

c Whether a green space is calm or noisy will have an obvious impact on its value as a green "oasis" or "sanctuary". This rating should be used as a measure of "external" noise affecting the tranquility of the green space – essentially traffic noise.

d This is an aspect of green space management which obviously touches on both design (furniture) and aesthetics – litter is usually paper/plastic bags, cups... but often includes bottles/cans...

e The items above relate to specific features. In (e) give your overall impression – how attractive is the green space itself and within its immediate urban fabric?

13 Other Information

(Briefly note any other aspects that you consider to be of interest. Is there any vandalism evident for instance?).

Table 3.2 The system of scoring used to calculate a rurality index for selected open spaces in the City of London.

Component		Attributed Score
Abundance of trees	1 - 5	1
	6 - 10	2
	> 10	3
Variety of trees	1 - 4	1
	5 - 8	2
	> 9	3
Percentage area vegetated	60 - 75	1
	76 - 90	2
	90 +	3
Presence of shrubs		1
Presence of grass		1
Presence of flowers		1
Precence of birds		1

Total Score
highest possible for any one green space = **13**

It is used several times in this report: for calculating the 'oasis' effect within City green spaces (p.39) it is compared with vegetational diversity and it is used in a composite evaluation of City open spaces.

Where appropriate the surveys of open space use (1985/6) have been compared with the results for the same areas as recorded in the Corporation of London (1970) *Pedestrian Movement Survey.*

The inventory of City trees within the report has been compiled from the initial City-wide surveys and from information provided by the Corporation of London Tree Record File (updated to 1976). This inventory was used to provide the data to calculate tree densities for the survey squares.

New surveys such as noise levels in open spaces and the Bird Survey have been directly incorporated into the report.

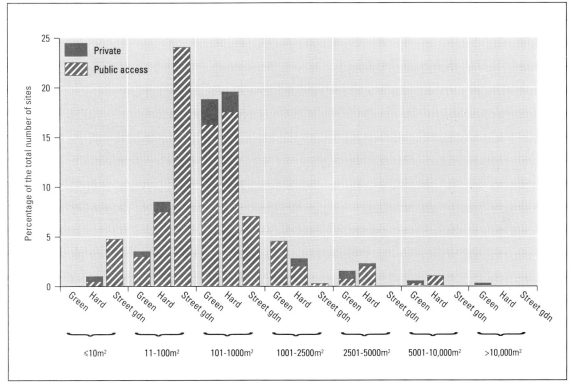

Figure 3.1   The size distributions of the three main categories of open space used in this study expressed as percentages of 357 sites.

Comment

With the compilation of the inventory sheets for individual squares following the initial City-wide survey some errors and omissions became evident. These were largely eliminated in the verification survey which followed. It should be noted, however, that some error must be expected in surveys undertaken by a large number of individual surveyors. Difficulties arose with regard to true species identification and true age estimation. Area measurements derived from field observation or map measurement may contain small inaccuracies; however, these are likely to be self cancelling in overall terms. Some difficulty was experienced in deciding the precise definition of street gardens, and some larger areas such as isolated traffic island gardens which cannot function as recreational green space have been incorporated into this category. The aesthetic rating (with some guidance provided in the survey briefing) is based on the subjective judgement of

individuals. Nevertheless, it permits a rapid and reasonably accurate, if necessarily generalized and rather simplistic aesthetic assessment, after a brief examination, for each open space.

The data provided by the inventory and map survey make it possible to gain a rapid overall picture of the City's open spaces in terms of their size, characteristics, overall area covered and distribution. This makes possible a brief comparative survey of City open spaces with those immediately to the west and east of the City's boundaries and to compare the City situation with that of an outer London borough.

It is especially useful to identify those areas of the City which, for one reason or another, are particularly well endowed with open spaces and those areas of the City which lack open spaces. In the latter case particular care needs to be exercised to retain both the number and area of open spaces which presently exist and, when-

ever redevelopment allows, to encourage their extension.

The individual base maps and inventory sheets for the
City-wide survey together with details of the special
surveys on which the results and discussion in this book
have been based are lodged with the City of London
Polytechnic Geography Department.

Survey Results

Number of Open Spaces

357 open spaces were identified in the City of London
in this survey. Street gardens accounted for 128 open
spaces (approximately 36%); there were 125 hard
spaces (35%); and 104 green spaces (29%). Access to
open space is obviously confined to hard and green
spaces, but it should be noted that a number of green
and hard spaces are closed to the general public, and
while their numbers are relatively small (Fig. 3.1), they
include some of the largest. Overall, green space without public access accounts for some 37,249 m² or 18%
area of the open space in the City but only 4.5% (16

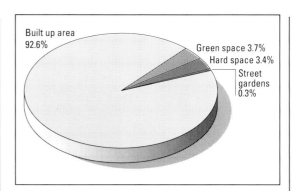

Figure 3.2   Relative proportions of built-up area and
three types of open space within the
total area of the City of London.

sites) of the total number of open spaces in the City.

Area of Open Space within the City

The total area of the City of London is 2,740,000 m²,
of which 202,143.1 m² (7.4%) is classified as open
space in the terms of this survey. Overall the area of
open space available to the public is 147,586.3 m² or
5.4% of the total land area of the City. A further 1.6%
(44,813.4 m²) is classified as private open space. Hard
space and green space occupy approximately the same

Table 3.3   Numbers and areas of green and hard open spaces and of street gardens within the City of London.

	GREEN SPACES		HARD SPACES		STREET GARDENS	Total No. of Sites and area
	Open*	Closed*	Open	Closed		
Number of Sites (% total)	88 (24.6)	16 (4.5)	111 (31.1)	14 (3.9)	128 (35.9)	357
Total Area (m²) (% total)	63326.9 31.3	37249.0 18.4	84259.4 41.7	7564.4 3.7	9742.4 4.8	202,142.1
Mean Area for Sites (m²)	719.6	2328.1	759.1	540.3	76.1	
Range (m²)	14.0 - 4776.7	62.4 - 16879.2	4.7 - 6347.6	6.2 - 2968.7	6.2 - 1154.0	
Mean Range (m²)	130.7 - 1631.9	668.2 - 3031.9	119.2 - 2664.5	493.4 - 644.4	18.9 - 255.8	

*Open – Open to general public
*Closed – Closed to general public (private)

area but significantly there is a considerably greater area of hard space open to the public than green space (Table 3.3). The overall area occupied by street gardens, as might be expected, represents a very small overall area, some 9,740 m², only 5% of the total area of open spaces in the City.

Mean Area of Open Space

The mean area per site for green spaces open to the public is 719.6 m² and for green spaces closed to the general public 2,328.1 m² (Table 3.3). The largest open spaces with unimpeded access to the public are represented by hard spaces; these have a mean area of 759.1 m². Hard spaces closed to the public have a mean of 540.3 m² per site. In contrast, the average area per site of street gardens is only 76.1 m²; however, this is to be expected. Therefore, the mean size of green areas closed to the general public is three times as great as the next largest mean, that of hard space open to the

general public.

Range of Open Space Sizes

The greatest range of sizes of open spaces is within the green 'closed' space category; the smallest range is represented by street gardens (Table 3.3). A more useful method of assessing the ranges of figures and giving a clearer picture of the overall situation, is to take the mean of both lower and upper ranges. The greatest mean range is for hard 'open' space (119.2 - 2664.5 m²) and the smallest for hard 'closed' spaces (493.4 - 644.4 m²); these correspond to the largest and smallest total area of land, respectively. Some interesting points may be noted from the figures in Table 3.3. The category of smallest size is hard 'closed' spaces, even though they tend to have a larger size than street gardens. The largest open space is a green 'closed' area of some 16,879.2 m², namely Inner Temple and Middle Temple Gardens. The lowest mean range area is 18.9 m² for street gardens and the highest 3,031.9 m² for green 'closed' areas.

Open Spaces in Size Categories

The highest number of open spaces in any size class is that of street gardens in the 11-100 m² class, 85 in total (Fig. 3.1), while the highest number of green and hard spaces (both open and closed) can be found in the 10 -1000 m² class, comprising 58 green 'open' spaces, 63 hard 'open' spaces, 9 green 'closed' spaces and 7 hard 'closed' spaces. No green space is less than or equal to 10 m²; however, green spaces are recorded in all other size classes. Hard space is recorded in all but the largest size category, while street gardens, as may be expected, are not present in size classes above 2501 m².

Vegetation Structure of Open Spaces

The 357 open spaces surveyed indicate a dominance of trees and shrubs, which are found in over 300 open spaces, while only 120 have grassed areas (Fig. 3.3).

Vegetational Structure of Street Gardens

A random sample of 40 street gardens was carried out in order to ascertain their vegetational structure. These

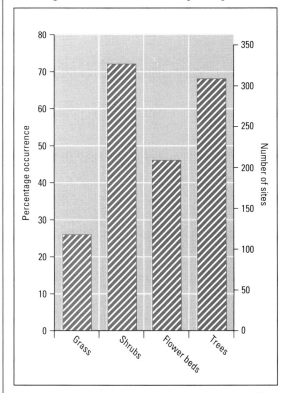

Figure 3.3   The frequency of occurrences of different vegetation types within 357 open spaces in the City of London.

sites contained from one to three types of vegetation. Seven (17.5%) of the sites contained only flowers. Only 2 sites (5%) contained trees alone, and only 3 (7.5%) shrubs alone. More sites had a combination of trees and shrubs, 11 (27.5%), than contained a combination of either flowers and shrubs, 5 (12.5%), or flowers and trees, 3 (7.5%). Overall, trees and shrubs formed the largest group of vegetation structure types within street gardens. The next largest group, of 9 sites (22.5%), involved a combination of all three structure types within the street garden.

Design and Aesthetic Rating of Open Spaces

Within each open space the total scores for each attribute were averaged to give a City-wide rating, and the results are shown in Table 3.4. The figure for the mean of the five attributes recorded is 2.6.

Table 3.4   The mean scores (for all open spaces in the City of London) for the five attribute scales contributing to the Design and Aesthetic ratings.

Attribute Scale	Mean
urban-rural	1.70
incongruous-harmonious	2.78
noisy-calm	2.24
littered-tidy	3.55
dull-attractive	2.85

It can be seen that City green spaces are generally judged to be attractive 'green features'. As might be expected, the small spaces with limited green cover, typical of the City, are unlikely to heighten a 'rural' illusion, thus the mean score on this scale is low. Similarly, these spaces are hardly well insulated from the noise, air and visual pollution associated with City traffic (see chapter 7). On the other hand the design and 'green space architecture' are generally judged appropriate and sympathetic, while the high standard of green space maintenance across the City is emphasised by the highest mean score.

The Rurality of Open Spaces

For a random selection of 8 City grid squares the mean

rurality index scores were calculated; the City-wide mean was 8.64, the mean scores ranging from 6.33 (square 12) to 11.50 (square 15). This range is to be expected; square 15 scores highly because of the presence of the tree-filled and extensive Temple gardens which are the largest green space in the City. In contrast, square 12, at the centre of the core area of the City, has very few green spaces, and this is reflected in the lowest rurality score of 6.33.

The Distribution of Open Space

The distribution of open space within the City, that is, the three major categories, was analysed within the core area, as defined in the City of London Information Report entitled 'Offices 1982' (Corporation of London 1984), and the area around it, namely the periphery. The total core area was calculated at 744,129 m^2 (27.2% of the total area of the City) and the area of the periphery 1,995,871m^2 (72.8% of the total area of the City).

Open space in the core was calculated at 40,356.1 m^2. Therefore, only 20% of the total City open space is to be found in the core area of the City. This in fact represents a deficiency of open space, since the core is calculated to represent 27.2% of the total area of the City.

Breaking these figures down, the core comprises 27,730.8 m^2 or 30.2% of total hard space area in the City; 11,163.9 m^2 or 11.1% of the total City green space area; and 1,461.4 m^2 or 15% of total street gardens area. Thus, when comparing these figures with the total area of the City there is proportionally a slightly greater amount of hard space. However, on a proportional basis, there are major deficiencies of both green space and street gardens within the core of the City.

Hard surface in the periphery totals 64,093 m^2 or 69.8% of the total hard space area; 89,412.2 m^2 or 88.9% of the total green space area; and 8,281.0 m^2 or 85.0% of the total area of street gardens are in the periphery. Therefore, in total, 161,786.2 m^2 of open space is found in the periphery. This figure represents 80% of all open spaces and therefore consists of a

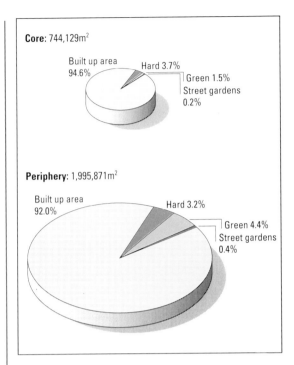

Figure 3.4   A comparison of the percentages of total land area occupied by three types of open space in the core (top) and peripheral (bottom) parts of the City of London.

proportionately larger area than the figure of 72.8% for the total area of the City.

As can be seen from the above figures, the greater percentage of open space within the periphery is largely due to the many green spaces and street gardens found there, while the figure for hard space is proportionately more in line with the core area.

Since the areas involved in this analysis are very different (the periphery area is approximately 2.5 times the area of the core), it was considered necessary, for comparative purposes, to calculate open space as a percentage of total land area of both the core and the periphery (Fig. 3.4).

A greater amount of hard space as a percentage of total land area is present in the core area, whereas higher percentages of both green space and street gardens are found in the periphery. The most striking feature of

these results is the very considerable amount of green space as a percentage of total land area in the periphery, compared with the core (three times as much green space).

68.7 per cent of the open space in the core consists of hard surface areas, whereas the figure is only 39.6 per cent in the periphery. 27.7 per cent of the core is green space, but in the periphery the figure is almost double this amount, 55.3 per cent. In both cases street gardens are a comparatively small component, 3.6 per cent in the core and 5.1 per cent in the periphery.

A more detailed spatial analysis of the distribution of open space within the City can be gained from an examination of Figs. 3.5-3.7. These maps show the areal distribution of the various types of open space within the City. The greater amount of green open space found in the periphery is highlighted in Fig. 3.5. This map also shows that green space is not spread evenly throughout the City. Areas with considerable amounts of green space in the periphery include Inner Temple and Middle Temple Gardens (21,710.2 m²) situated in the extreme south west of the City and largely without public access (number **1** in Fig. 3.5); the Barbican complex (8,283.6 m²) to the north of the City (**2**), and again largely private; St. Paul's (4,776.7 m²) immediately to the west of the core (**3**); and Finsbury Circus (7,284.0 m²) to the north east of the City (**4**). These two latter sites are both open to the public and are nearest to the core. Smaller areas of green space are found throughout the remaining peripheral area.

Areas that show a distinct lack of green space can be identified as the extreme west of the City and the area concentrated in the north west. Two of the largest green spaces are at the corner of Aldermanbury and Love Lane (904.8 m² – **A** in Fig. 3.5) and along Noble Street (2,284 m² – **B** in Fig. 3.5). There are few other green spaces within the remainder of the core, the south east and central areas of the core being particularly deficient (see Fig. 3.5).

More hard space than green space can be found in the core (see above). Three large areas comprise approximately a third of the total hard space within the core

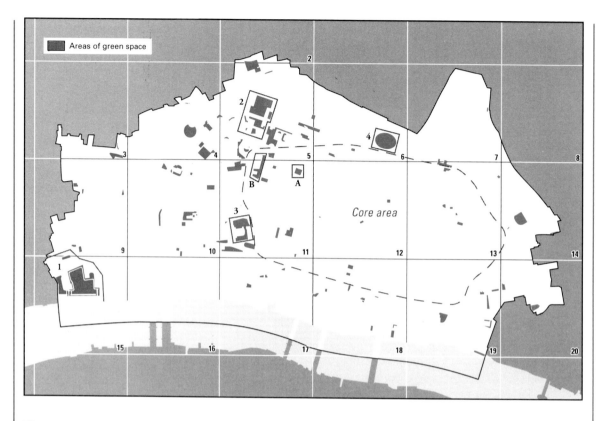

Figure 3.5   The location of green open spaces throughout the City of London. The dotted line demarcates the core area (see text).

(see Fig. 3.6), namely to the south of the Guildhall (2,927.7 m²) to the north west of the core (**A** in Fig. 3.6), the corner of New Change and Watling Street (2,028.0 m²) to the west of the core (**B**) and the corner of Leadenhall Street and St. Mary Axe (3,619.2 m²) in the east of the City (**C**). The remaining area is comprised of considerably smaller units found throughout the core. However, as Fig. 3.6 shows, the areas to the north west and south have a deficiency of hard space.

There are several large areas of hard space located in the periphery. In the north east, between Harrow Place, New Street and Middlesex Street, is an area of 6,347.6 m² (number **1** in Fig. 3.6); a similar area can be found in the south east of the City by Byward Street (**2**); Paternoster Square, practically adjacent to St. Paul's, has a total area of 5,778.2 m² (**3**); and the area adjacent to Brittania House to the north of the City comprises 5,369 m² (**4**). Two 'clusters' of land space can be found

in the periphery. One is comprised of Brick Court, Pump Court, Hare Court, Church Court and Temple Church (3,709.7 m² in total), located to the west of the City, and is associated with the Inns of Court and the Temple areas. The second is within the Barbican complex, comprising Bunyan Court, Bridgewater Street, Concert Hall, and St Giles Church. This area is located to the north of the City (**6** in Fig. 3.6) and totals 1,401.4 m². There are two notable areas of the periphery that are deficient in hard space: these are in the north west and along the Embankment.

As Fig. 3.7 shows, the majority of street gardens are located outside the core, including the larger areas of street gardens. Gardens are distributed more evenly throughout the periphery, although they are less evident in the extreme south west and northern areas. The largest street gardens in the periphery are Devonshire Square (293.3 m², in Fig. 3.7), and around Sedgewick

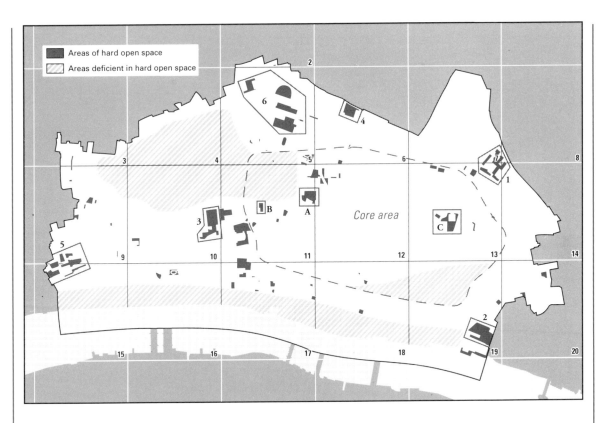

Figure 3.6   The location of hard open spaces in the City of London. The dotted line demarcates the core area (see text) and the hatched areas are those deficient in hard open spaces.

Forbes House (488.6 m², **2**), both located in the eastern area of the City; and Victoria Embankment (173.2 m², **3**), Farringdon Street (173.2 m², **4**), Holborn Viaduct (93.6 m², **5**), Seacole Lane (87.4 m², **6**) and Fleet Lane (187.2 m², **7**), all located in the western part of the City.

Three of the largest areas of street gardens within the core are along Aldermanbury (129.5 m² **A** in Fig. 3.7); at the corner where Old Broad Street meets Wormwood (70.2 m², **B**); and along Bishopsgate (31.2 m², **C**). The remaining street gardens are generally smaller and located near the outer boundary of the core. Thus the central area of the core is deficient in street gardens.

Comparison with other London Boroughs

Before examining the role of green spaces in the City of

London, it is useful to look briefly at selected London Boroughs in relation to the City to illustrate points of similarity and difference in the context of London as a whole. The boroughs selected were Tower Hamlets, Kensington and Chelsea, and Harrow.

Tower Hamlets lies immediately to the east of the City of London. It has a total area of 2,021 hectares of which 6.4 per cent is public open space, including a part of Victoria Park on the northern boundary and the developing Mile End Park in the south-east.

Kensington and Chelsea lies immediately to the west of the City of Westminster and five miles from the City of London. In total the borough comprises an area of 1,195 hectares of which 64.5 hectares (5.4 per cent of the total area) is public parks and open spaces.

The outer London Borough of Harrow is essentially a

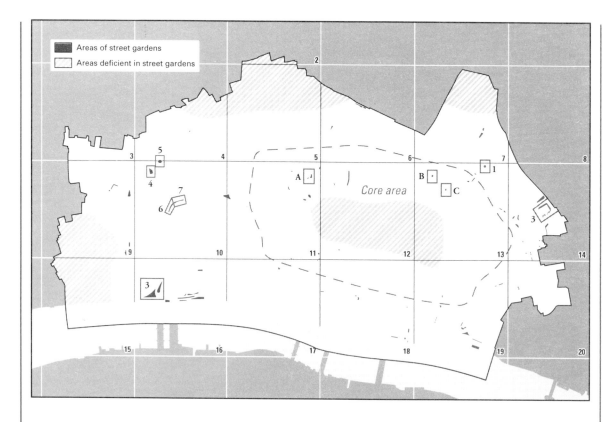

Figure 3.7   The location of street gardens in the City of London. The dotted line demarcates the core area (see text) and the hatched areas are those deficient in street gardens.

residential area of 5,080 hectares. It has the greatest amount of public open space not only as a percentage (Table 3.5) but also in absolute terms (see Fig. 3.8). This reflects a situation that might be expected given distance from the city and location on the periphery of London.

A remarkable percentage of total land area is designated as open space in the City of London, a figure above those of Kensington and Tower Hamlets. This figure is particularly interesting as it demonstrates the importance of the green element, as an essential part in the city's townscape.

It should be mentioned, however, that the definition of public open space may vary slightly from borough to borough. In addition, the figures that are referred to for the City of London include both public and private

open space, while figures for the other boroughs do not include the latter. It is also important to specify that domestic open space in the City is almost non-existent, while it represents a considerable area in outer boroughs and may approximate to 50 per cent of the total land area in an outer London Borough such as Harrow.

The capital and revenue expenditures are given for the same selected boroughs (Table 3.5) based on some published information and personal communications, they should be interpreted with some caution as the areas and expenditures to which they refer are slightly different. In global terms the City's green space expenditure is the smallest. This would be expected given the small overall area (and the fact that some open spaces are privately maintained). The high expenditure in Tower Hamlets in 1985/6 represented a considerable input for renovation and creation of green space,

Table 3.5   Comparison of open space and expenditure thereon between three London Boroughs and the City of London.

	Total Area (Hectares)	Total Open Space (Hectares)	% Open Space	Budget and Revenue (£)	Amount Spent on Each Hectare of Open Space (£) (amount per Hectare)	Population	Open Space per Inhabitant (m²)
Kensington	1,195	64.47	5.39	628,000 1984/5	9,741	136,800	4.71
Tower Hamlets	2,021	130.00	6.43	3,595,700 1985/6	27,659	144,500	9.00
Harrow	5,080	426.22	8.39	1,659,530 1985/6	3,893	198,800	21.44
City of London	274	20.21	7.38	578,000 1984/5	28,599	Day 340,000	0.59

while the relatively low figure for Harrow is partly explained by the lower cost associated with the maintenance of the borough's considerable area of parkland, compared to gardens and other more expensive forms of green urban space.

Continuing restraints on public spending have been

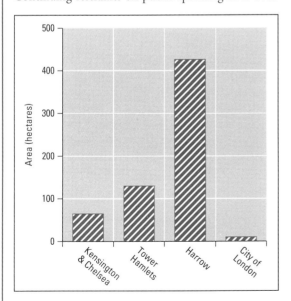

Figure 3.8   Comparison of the area of open space in three London Boroughs and the City of London.

rigorous and expenditure on open spaces is probably more constrained than in other areas of local government expenditure. In addition, it should be remembered that gardens, particularly, are labour intensive and costly to maintain.

As Table 3.5 shows, the capital plus revenue expenditure figures for open space differ quite remarkably from borough to borough. The City of London spends least, Tower Hamlets at £3,595,700 spends most. Perhaps a more appropriate way of expressing these particular figures would be the amount spent on each hectare of open space. Quite a different picture emerges from these results (Fig. 3.9), with the City of London spending most per hectare whereas Harrow spends least per hectare. Thus although the City of London has the smallest capital and revenue expenditure figures of all the selected boroughs, it spends the most on a per hectare basis.

The amount of open space per inhabitant (Table 3.5) also shows extremely large differences between the selected boroughs. Harrow has as much as 21.4 m² per inhabitant whereas the City of London only has 0.6 m² per inhabitant (daytime population). This latter figure differs quite considerably from the 2.8 – 3.7 m² range of greenspace per inhabitant, as calculated by Van Rooden (1983) for the centre of Rotterdam. However,

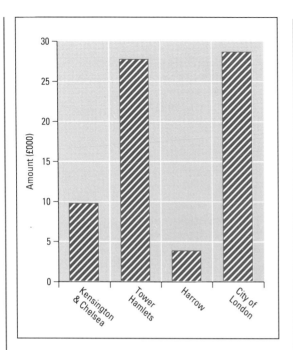

Figure 3.9 Expenditure per hectare (years given in Table 3.5) on open space in three London Boroughs and the City of London.

he included residential areas which are not included in the figures for Kensington and Chelsea, Harrow and Tower Hamlets. If these figures were available it is probable that the figures would be comparable with those for the Rotterdam area and would heighten the difference between these boroughs and the City of London.

If the City is further compared with two neighbouring areas of roughly equal size – a part of Tower Hamlets (250 ha) and the 'West End' (i.e. part of the City of Westminster, 200 ha), the total number of open spaces identified within each area is considerably different. As well as having a high percentage of land area designated as open space the City has more open spaces than these other two areas (Table 3.6). Indeed the City has over four times as many as the West End, 357 compared to 83.

Table 3.6 gives numbers and percentages of the different types of open space. This shows that the majority, over 60 per cent, of open space in the City of London is designated as green space, whereas over 60 per cent is designated as hard space in the West End. There is no

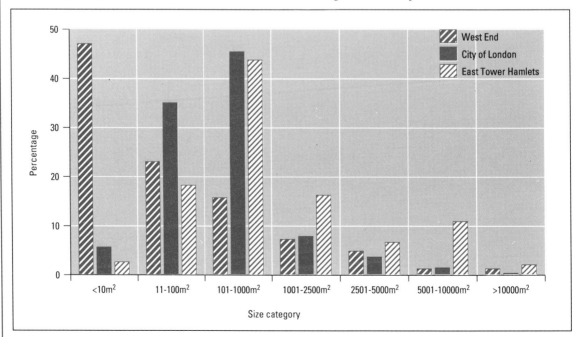

Figure 3.10 Comparison between the City of London and two adjacent areas, of approximately the same size, in the size distributions of their open spaces.

Table 3.6   Comparison of information on open spaces in the City of London with that from two adjacent areas of approximately equal size, the West End (part of the City of Westminster) and part of the London Borough of Tower Hamlets. (%)

		West (West End)	City of London	East (Tower Hamlets)
1	Total Area Examined	200 ha	274 ha	250 ha
2	Number of Open Spaces	83	357	334
3	Number and Percentage of Open Spaces of Type			
	(a) Hard	55 (66.3)	125 (35.0)	50 (15.0)
	(b) Formal/Green (inc street gardens)	26 (31.3)	232 (65.0)	228 (68.3)
	(c) Vacant/Other	2 (2.4)	0 (0)	56 (16.7)
4	Number of Open Spaces:			
	(a) Open	54 (65.0)	144 (87.8)	215 (64.4)
	(b) Closed	29 (35.0)	20 (12.2)	119 (35.6)
5	Total Number of Trees	1162	1885	2916
6	Number of Occurences of Plane Trees	154 (13.3)	425 (22.6)	367 (12.6)
7	Design & Aesthetic Rating – Mean Value			
	(a) Urban/Rural	2.65	1.70	1.96
	(b) Incongruous/Harmonious	2.89	2.78	2.65
	(c) Noisy/Calm	2.87	2.24	2.89
	(d) Littered/Tidy	3.21	3.55	3.26
	(e) Dull/Attractive	2.97	2.85	2.44
		2.92	2.62	2.64

vacant land in the City of London itself, and very little in the West End (2.4 per cent). By contrast, Tower Hamlets has the highest proportion of vacant land and the lowest proportion of hard space.

A comparison between the percentages of open space size categories in the different areas can be seen on Fig. 3.10. This shows that the West End has considerably more open spaces in the smallest category than in any other, indeed most open spaces in the West End are very small. However, it is interesting to note that in both the City and Tower Hamlets this particular category represents one of the smallest percentages. Contrary to what could be expected within a heavily built up financial centre, the City of London shows a comparatively large number of green open spaces when compared to its immediate neighbours.

Railway Place prior to redevelopment.

CHAPTER 4

Open Spaces and Townscape

This chapter looks at several aspects of the architectural – visual contribution open spaces and street trees make to the City's townscape. The architectural role of green space, hard space and street gardens is demonstrated with reference to specific sites. No one can fail to be impressed by the visual significance one significant tree can have in a street otherwise devoid of greenery. The value of street trees is assessed by highlighting the ways in which such trees significantly characterise the street scene. Cities have often been described as 'garden cities' or 'green oases'. By means of an index of rurality this chapter examines the degree to which the City's green spaces create an illusion of *rus in urbe*. If City open spaces illustrate one thing above all others it is their rich diversity and so brief consideration is given to their classification and, in conclusion, a typology of city open spaces is suggested based on the threefold division which forms the basis of this survey.

The Architectural Role of City Open Spaces

Open spaces undoubtedly make a major contribution to the architectural landscape or townscape of the City. In an area of high building density but low residential population, open spaces, particularly green spaces, add an element of human scale and proportion to the overall building scene, so visually moderating the 'canyon-street' image that the more monolithic office blocks increasingly give to parts of the City and providing space that has aesthetic as well as recreational 'returns' especially important in the City's high pressure environment. Their contributions to the townscape are varied.

- Open spaces can increase the perceived size of an area, so enlarging cramped conditions. Trees can augment this effect, giving an impression of greater space than is actually available (Fairbrother 1974).

- Different surface treatment of open spaces, whether they are natural or artificial, produces variations in colour, pattern, shade and texture, which may enhance or conflict with the adjacent architecture.

- Time is an important factor, as the contribution that open spaces make to the townscape will change according to their age. As an open space becomes older, it is more likely that the trees and shrubs will be sufficiently mature and dominant to register as City 'architecture'. In addition, the long established open spaces of the City are generally more integrated with surrounding buildings, especially if the buildings are more recent than the space, and their effect on the space has been taken into account during their design.

- The significance of the architectural character of an open space may be appreciated from many different aspects, so that the transitory visual contribution that open spaces make towards the townscape will be largely dependent on the position of the observer. If buildings are viewed from within a green space, or through trees, the effect will be different than if they are viewed from without. It is therefore important to consider the overall architectural contribution resulting from these two positions.

Green Spaces

Green spaces provide greater potential for architectural contrast and enhancement than any other type of open space in the City. Their general function may be regarded as primarily to provide an enclosed area for relaxation, lunch or resting, rather than for simply walking through. This function allows for a hierarchy of vegetation (Lloyd 1979) ranging from lawns and small shrubs to bushes and trees. The presence of grass provides one of the most obvious visual contrasts to surrounding architecture. As with hard spaces, however, there are a number of elements that need to be described in order to define how exactly the green spaces affect the architecture and help to develop the characterisation of 'place'. These will be examined using the example of Finsbury Circus.

Finsbury Circus is the largest and best known of the City's green spaces. A considerable variety of floorscape is found within it. Short grass makes up the majority of the area. In addition, there is the bowling green which, being more formal, complements the similar formal building frontages overlooking the green space. The tarmac path running around the open space provides contrast in terms of colour and texture. There are, in addition, contrasting levels at the west entrance seating area which is also paved. There are no planters in Finsbury Circus because the bushes, shrubs and flowers can be placed straight into the ground, providing contrast with the grass at the same level. There is considerable variety in both species and age which contrasts well with the surounding architectural styles. The various types of hedges that border the area give a sense of enclosure although they do not totally block out the buildings. Within the area there are multiple foci; the bowling green is probably the major one, yet a number of trees and shrubs are sufficiently dominant in size or shape to constitute points of interest. Nevertheless the layout is such that it does not appear cluttered but distinctly planned which gives this green space immediate character.

Garden buildings within the green space provide another element of interest. The dominant ones are the less than attractive clubhouse for the bowling club, the bandstand, and an enclosed drinking water fountain. The latter two features give character to this space.

The seating consists of standard wooden benches which are unobtrusive and functional. The number of litter bins is consistent with the number of benches. The surrounding iron railings highlight the age and historical quality of the area contained. (Modern designed spaces tend not to have them made in such ornate forms as the earlier Victorian ones.) The low fencing around the bowling green is unobtrusive and serves merely to discourage people from wandering onto the green accidentally.

It is the trees that make the most significant visual contribution to the architecture of this green space. There are many, and their height indicates that they are probably some of the most mature trees in the City. As a result of this there is also great variation in patterning, colour and ground shading, ranging from very dense to light-dappled according to both the season and the species. There is also a softening effect of the trees on the surrounding architecture, the regularity is broken up and the formality is reduced as a result. The trees around the periphery help to diffuse the actual boundary of the green space, giving an impression of more space beyond.

As noted earlier, the overall impression of a green space depends very much on the position of the viewer. Finsbury Circus probably has the greatest number of vantage points from which to admire the layout. As a result the 'effectiveness' of the space is high in terms of visual impact. Views outside are restricted due to the trees and also because the seating faces inwards.

Finsbury Circus today presents a dramatic 'architectural contrast' to the buildings which surround the Circus. Nevertheless the overall effect is to enhance the whole. The green space is of sufficient scale and diversity to be a major townscape feature. It is self contained and its many interesting features provide a highly valuable recreational space.

Since the creation of Finsbury Circus the trees have matured; this means that 'aesthetically' they may well be at their best. However, the implications for continuance are not all positive. For instance, no new saplings have been planted to replace the present large mature trees as will be necessary eventually. If the present trees are not selectively replaced by trees of a similar size over a period of time the surrounding buildings will dominate the green and the unique sense of enclosure will be lost. Also a change will have taken place in the architectural balance of the area since at the moment the trees are the dominant element.

Hard Spaces

As part of the architectural fabric of the City and as distinct from street corridors, hard spaces contribute greatly to spatial variety. For practical reasons (such as easier maintenance), more hard space is retained than green open spaces.

Their durability makes them appropriate for much trafficked areas, as Cullen (1983) has noted: 'paving emphasises the pedestrian nature of these places, more so than the preservation of a few square feet of sooty turf'. The function of these hard open spaces is also significant: generally, if the essential needs are for pedestrian route-ways, then less enclosure is needed; however, if the need is for rest and recreation or eating areas, a greater sense of enclosure is required. In order to assess the architectural impact of hard open spaces, four elements will be considered in relation to two examples from the City – Paternoster Square and Railway Place, Fenchurch Street Station.

The first and perhaps most important element is the floorscape. Paternoster Square is characterised by a very large expanse of concrete paving slabs with no special patterning, textural finish or colour variations anywhere on the Square. Having once climbed the steps on the south side of the Square from St Paul's, the whole area is on the same level. On the edge of the Square are planters containing small shrubs and flowers which make up a second element of the hard space. These are quite large, yet compared to the scale of the buildings and floorscape they appear to be much smaller. There are no central planters or any similar containers in the middle of the Square but only on the edges. They are square, and being off white they do not contrast with the grey paving and building colours.

Trees are present, but as they are all contained in planters their height and spread is restricted so that their architectural impact is restricted and their effectiveness as regards shade potential or as visual foils is low, as is their overall significance. Trees only realise this potential if their growth is sufficient to register on the scale of the buildings (Fairbrother 1974).

The 'street furniture' in the Square is the final element to consider and it includes the seating. This is formally arranged next to the planters, facing inward across the dull floorscape and without a particular focus. The benches are made of dark brown wood and are of a very simple design. Other features are the lights, which are tall and of a modern design with three round units at alternate heights. These are in keeping with the modern architecture, but do not particularly help to characterise the Square itself. There are a few other features: some signs and litter bins, but nothing that succeeds in characterising the Square and providing it with a focus.

Having looked at the various elements that go to make up Paternoster Square, the overall effectiveness of the hard space needs to be considered. There seems to be a conflict, partly because the purpose of the Square seems ambiguous. Certainly if it is only used as a thoroughfare then large scale paving is functional. However, the proximity of St Paul's means that this hard space may be used recreationally, in which case a number of changes would be desirable.

In architectural terms the Square will (and has frequently) come under scrutiny. The lack of contrast between the paving and buildings leads to a visual continuum, with the large planar surface being accentuated by the monolithic building frontages. Patterning or textural variation is one way in which this problem may be overcome. Similarly, the location and size of the planters do little to alleviate the overall impression of barrenness. A central focus could provide the answer without appearing banal. The views from the Square are determined by the position of the observer and whilst there is a lot of scope for movement within the Square, actual views out are restricted to the north. The main focus is, therefore, St Paul's, yet even this is far from inspiring due to the surrounding office development. The presence of larger mature trees would be effective in 'unifying' the old and new architecture but would be difficult to locate in engineering terms.

Unhappily the square is hardly an effective use of open space. It does little to enhance the grid-iron of indistinguished buildings which surround it. In part this is due to its inappropriate layout, ill defined spatial function and also to its lack of a simple focus. Even large scale planters could have done something to alleviate the feeling of monotony so that even the limited architectural potential of the area would not have been dissipated.

Thought needs to be given to the possible improvements over time that might take place. It seems unlikely that they will come through any 'maturing' processes of either the modern architecture or vegetation, therefore re-development is the most effective option; indeed at the present time, it seems that this will occur. However desirable improvements on the present site would be, they can only be of limited value. Over a number of years many voices have suggested redevelopment of the area as the most effective option for environmental enhancement. In 1991 Paternoster Associates submitted plans for such a comprehensive redevelopment of this site. According to their plans, in terms of layout and style the buildings suggested would achieve a better harmonisation of buildings with St. Paul's Cathedral while at the same time providing for a series of public walkways with associated intimate forecourts together with a central hard surfaced square.

Railway Place forms a forecourt to Fenchurch Street Station. It is a much smaller hard space than Paternoster Square and is different in function and atmosphere. The function of this space is easier to determine; it is primarily used as a thoroughfare, although it is also used as a resting place for travellers using the Station and for office workers having lunch.

This area has been redeveloped since the initial survey and is a good example of changes which occur to City open spaces from time to time.

The most striking feature of the present space is its floorscape composed of small brown sets relieved by bands of a lighter shade giving, overall, a striped effect. This accentuates the pedestrian 'walkway' theme, at the same time associating the area with a specific purpose.

The major features are a number of large raised circular planters made from similar materials to the floor. In the main these planters protect and enclose some of the larger trees which have remained after redevelopment. There is one larger elmgate planter used as an attractive flower bed. It focuses the major feature and divides the area, one suspects to no very great purpose except to form a backdrop for some of the seating in Railway Place.

Trees contribute to the overall architecture in various ways, being sufficiently mature to form a visual foil for the Station in terms of colour, pattern and texture. However, the plain wall to the north is only partially shaded by low trees and bushes which are found in a low planter against the wall. Furthermore the lack of seating here seems to be a lost opportunity. This is surprising, as this feature must be the least encouraging architectural aspect of the space, and is the most in need of attention.

Various items of street furniture are found in Railway Place, such as additional square wooden planters for floor display, new blue metal seats surrounding some of the trees which are not in planters, while litter bins are located near the Station entrance. On the elmgate planter there is a modern sign for the station which seems incongruous when compared with the station's 'traditional' appearance. A number of bollards are sited on the Station side and these maintain the pedestrian nature of the space by keeping the area traffic-free.

Although Railway Place has been preserved it is not as pleasing, aesthetically, as it was before redevelopment. Previously it presented a simple harmony with a large central planter, focal to the open space as a whole. This feature was surrounded, towards the boundary of the area, by a number of small circular flower tub planters, while the floor space was pleasantly dapple- shaded by a number of strategically placed trees (see frontispiece for this Chapter).

One of the main reasons for the rather lacklustre appearance is the absence of a recognisable focal feature. Furthermore the southern perimeter is now poorly defined. The various styles of street furniture used, and their disposition, contribute to a rather cluttered image.

Nevertheless, despite these critisisms Railway Place remains a pleasant area and an effective hard space considering its relatively small size. Its effectiveness can be attributed, in part, to its clearly defined functions as a walkway, waiting area and summer lunch spot.

Street Gardens

Street gardens form a valuable contribution to both their adjacent architecture and the 'roadscape' of an area. There is a great variety of 'street gardens' in the City, ranging from small pavement feature, to segregational barriers and large traffic islands. A major function is that of a barrier, keeping traffic from pedestrian view, although there are some examples of the 'infilling' of spaces between carriageways and routeways.

The largest example of the latter in the City occurs near Blackfriars Bridge where an extensive area of grass and flower beds has been laid out. This street garden shows the effect that they can have on the adjacent architecture as well as on the roadscape. If the floorscape element is considered, the contrast between the turf and tarmac is immediately apparent. The textural variation between these two surfaces is very important, as it helps demarcate the open space from the road. This visual boundary line is significant as the area is virtually inaccessible to pedestrians due to the proximity of the road, and the gardens are generally only viewed from a distance. However, the roles of texture, shape and pattern play a secondary role to the dominance of colour as a contrasting feature. These gardens are predominantly green and so provide an excellent contrast with the road. From the normal pedestrian viewing distance only the larger bushes and trees stand out and make individual impacts, and it is the overall effect, especially the colour contrast, that has greater importance.

Although no planters are necessary at the Blackfriars street garden, other gardens such as at Aldgate are totally dependent on them due to the paved nature of the area. Where planters are used for street gardens, they are generally large single structures, their contents varying with their different functions: trees and shrubs are for screening traffic from pedestrians, while flowers are used for the visual enhancement of the roadscape. Street furniture in these gardens is usually in keeping with the nature of the space and consists mainly of signposts, traffic control lights and street lights, all for the benefit of the road user rather than the pedestrian. Little can be done to reduce the numbers of traffic signals and signs as the traffic in the City is so heavy, although Cullen (1983) argues that generally such street furniture could safely be reduced. The lack of seating is notable but is consistant with a street garden's function not as space for relaxation but a purely visual element.

Although the contrasting floorscape and the distinct furniture of street gardens are important, it is perhaps the trees which have the most significant architectural impact. If they are not in traffic sight lines, trees can reach appreciable heights, serving not only as visual foils, but also as street architecture in their own right. When looking west from the east side of the Blackfriars street gardens the impact of the trees on the buildings behind can be clearly seen; however, the effect of the trees changes with the angle from which they are viewed. Unlike most green spaces, the architectural impact must be viewed from outside the space as there is no access within it, therefore the position of the observer is limited to the adjacent pavements. The Blackfriars example is effective from a variety of pavement vantage points because of its extent and the simplicity of its layout, while adjacent buildings are partially hidden and their bulk is reduced by the trees in the green 'island'

Even though it is remote, this street garden is architecturally successful as it adds variety to what may otherwise have been a large expanse of concrete. The trees help to enhance the architecture of the buildings opposite in the same way as trees do in any green or hard space. Although there is potential for more maturing of the trees, limits may have to be placed on the heights and widths of trees in case they cause obstruction to traffic, and future developments will have to take this into account. The other vegetation present can continue to grow and enhance the open space more. Improved access to the space could be a possible development; if it were subsequently landscaped, traffic noise could be reduced and the more enclosed atmosphere could turn the area into a valuable green space.

The Architectural Role of Street Trees

As building design has evolved, the architectural role of trees has changed. In the past buildings were conceived as complete in themselves: they contained sufficient variety of texture and modelling in their façades to make them self-sufficient works of art. However, today's buildings are generally less intriguing to the eye and the need for enrichment is clear. Cullen (1983) suggests that 'the art of bringing trees and buildings together is based on the tree lending its richness to buildings, and on buildings pointing out the architectural qualities of trees so that together they make one ensemble'. Fairbrother (1974) describes how trees are the vegetation 'par excellence' for cities for two main reasons: firstly, their size allows them to register on the city scale of building; and secondly, their piloti structure (that is, their bulk) occupies high level space. This leads to the 'space modulation' of Brown (1983) 'looking through the trunks of trees modulates space and by providing a middle ground and a key to scale and distance, reinforces the sense of 'here and beyond'. It is by this characteristic, even in quite small spaces, that the presence of a tree creates an illusion of enlargement'.

Although aesthetic visual value is by no means the only benefit derived from street trees in the City, it is at once the most readily striking, yet least definable, role that they play. Aesthetic value is difficult to assess as individuals will react in different ways to the many effects trees have on the townscape. In addition, the value of a tree will vary with type, age and position, so that a direct objective comparison of street trees is difficult. Nevertheless a survey was attempted to try to achieve such a comparison of street tree values in the City.

Five streets were selected: London Wall, Gresham Street, Bucklersbury, Walbrook, and Lambeth Hill. Five factors

of visual impact to which street trees contributed were selected and applied to the individual trees using a simple points system after Helliwell (1967 & 1974). For each factor a maximum of 4 points could be scored, the factors were then multiplied together to derive an 'index of architectural value', the theoretical maximum overall score being 1024 points. This maximum score would indicate a sizable mature tree, providing interesting shade on pavements and/or buildings with proportions fitting to its location on a tree lined street. In reality only exceptional trees are likely to score over 500 points (see below).

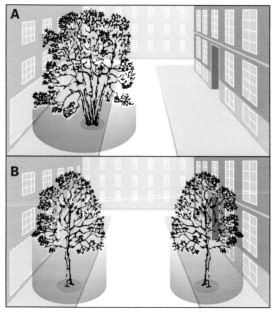

Figure 4.1   Measuring the visual impact of street trees: Canopy Overlap (CO).

The five factors considered were: canopy overlap (C.O.); green edge (G.E.); tree height; ground shading; and shade on buildings. These factors are explained below:

- **Canopy Overlap** is measured at right angles to buildings (see Fig. 4.1). The optimal C.O. (scoring 4 points) being in the range 41-60%. A significant C.O. of 31-40% scored 3 points, whereas moderate (21-30%) and restrictive (61-80%) scored 2 points. An insignificant (<20%) or obstructive (>80%) C.O. scored only 1 point. An optimal C.O. of 41 - 60% was used as this allows

Figure 4.2   The Green Edge (GE) was the longitudinal measure of the tree cover over the total length of the street or section surveyed (in this case inclusive of trees standing in green spaces). This edge was considered continuous if a gap between crowns of trees was less than half the crown diameter of the smaller tree.

maximum contrast between buildings and trees with no one factor dominating.

- **Green Edge** (G.E.) is the longitudinal measure of the tree cover over the total length of the street being surveyed. A continuous green edge was noted if a gap between tree crowns was less than half the diameter of the smaller tree (see Fig. 4.2). A G.E. of less than 30% scored 1, 31-50% scored 2, 51-70% scored 3, and greater than 70% scored a maximum 4.

- **Tree Height** was estimated in relation to the height of adjacent buildings (after Aldous 1979), points being awarded as follows: 50-120% of building height scored 4, over120% scored 3, 20-49% scored 2, and below 20% scored 1. The measure takes into account that a tree must reach a certain height before architectural impact is made.

- **Ground Shading:** The type of shading cast onto the ground by trees was noted and scored as follows: structured or dappled 4 points, dense shade 3 points, light shade 2 points, and where no shade was cast, for example due to adjacent tall buildings, 1 point was scored.

- **Shade on Buildings:** Again this was noted and scored on the following basis: structured or dappled scored 4 points, light shading 3 points, dense shade 2 points (in recognition of the local climate), no shade 1 point.

The maximum score attained in the survey was 384 points, scored by two fairly young London Plane trees in Walbrook. These scored maximum points in three out of the five criteria (C.O., height and ground shading). The lowest scores (2 points) were given to 6 trees; it is perhaps notable that these were all *Betula* sp.

In the sample the average score achieved was 81.8 points (see Table 4.1). Mean scores for each of the five streets surveyed were calculated to ascertain the architectural contribution of trees in single streets Table 4.1.

The highest mean (213.3) was achieved in Walbrook, a short street lined by six tall London plane trees. The scores

Table 4.1   Scores for the visual impact of street trees (derived as described in the text) in five streets of the City of London.

Street (section)	Number of trees	Total score	Mean score/tree	Trees/ 10m
London Wall East	4	196	49.0	
London Wall West	12	218	18.2	
All London Wall	**16**	**414**	**25.9**	**0.18**
Gresham St East	3	6	2.0	
Gresham St West	5	192	38.4	
All Gresham St	**8**	**198**	**24.8**	**0.17**
Bucklersbury	**4**	**512**	**128.0**	**1.0**
Walbrook	**6**	**1280**	**213.3**	**0.5**
Lambeth Hill East	2	16	8.0	
Lambeth Hill West	6	1016	169.3	
All Lambeth Hill	**8**	**1032**	**129.0**	**1.1**
All Streets	**42**	**3436**	**81.8**	**0.26**

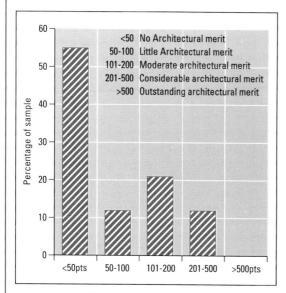

Figure 4.3   The percentage of a sample of 42 street trees scoring points in five categories of architectural value. (Data in Table 4.2; statistics in text.)

in this street ranged from 128 to 384 points, with four of the trees scoring 128 and two scoring 384, the difference being that the two higher scoring trees were able to cast some shade on the adjacent buildings whereas the four other trees could not do this. All six trees scored maximum points in three categories.

The section of London Wall between Moorgate and the Museum of London (London Wall West) scored very poorly. The twelve street trees in this section only averaging a score of 18.2, ranging from 2 to 32 points. The average for London Wall as a whole was slightly raised, to 25.9 by two London plane trees which stand between All Hallows on the Wall Church and Old Broad Street.

The trees in Gresham Street gave the lowest mean score, 24.8. The eastern section of Gresham Street was found to be devoid of trees of architectural value. Of the three trees in this section one was too young to make a significant contribution and the other two were small, unhealthy looking silver birches. These three trees depress the mean value for Gresham Street as a whole by scoring only a total of 2 points each. The six trees in Gresham Street West – average score 38.4 – are themselves too young to score highly while the lack of trees in a significant section of the street depresses the green edge value.

The six trees lining one side of Lambeth Hill West for approximately 25 m from the corner of Queen Victoria Street present a higher than average score, 169.3, which, however, might have been higher considering the maturity of the trees. While scoring highly on green edge and canopy overlap, their size and lack of ability to cast an interesting shade pattern on the adjacent buildings brings their average score down. The small size of these ornamental flowering cherry trees (*Prunus* sp.) means that they have little architectural impact when sited alongside tall buildings.

From these results it can be seen that great variations in street tree scores occur, even within the same street. In order to conclude an assessment of architectural impact, a ranking of the scores is needed. Scores over 22 points per tree would indicate considerable architectural impact. In such a case no one visual factor would have scored less than 1 point. Any score over 200 points means that all visual factors will have scored over 2 points. If two factors score exactly 2 then all the rest must achieve 5 points.

Only very exceptional trees will achieve scores of 500 points or more. The presence of one factor scoring only 2 means all the others must score maximum points to gain a total of 512. Scores of 100-200 indicate only one or two positive architectural characteristics. Either the tree has considerable shortcomings in all visual factors or it is a very young tree and as such is not reaching its full potential. Scores below 100 indicate no architectural impact due to very low scores in at least two factors. This occured with the two London plane trees in London Wall East, which scored poorly in green edge and on the shadow cast on adjacent buildings. In the sample of 42 trees, none were found to have an exceptional architectural value (Fig. 4.3). Five trees (12%) were of considerable value, 9 (21%) were of merit and 23 (54%) were of no architectural value. Over 25% of trees scored only 2 points. However, of those trees with low scores the majority were still saplings and so had not reached full potential. Over the next ten years they should achieve a marked improvement in all visual factors.

The value of such a survey is clear in that the impact of trees can now be evaluated and given a numerical score rather than just being considered in subjective terms. This helps to determine the relative merits of specific trees in their location and their effects on surrounding buildings. In addition, this approach could be applied elsewhere and regional impacts assesed. As Aldous (1979) says, 'tree planting can realize the full potential of external spaces by introducing new dimensions and perspectives.' This survey shows how this potential is extended to buildings as well.

'Rurality' and 'Oasis' within the City

As the green spaces of the City vary greatly in area, it is useful to consider whether this variation can directly affect their individual vegetational and environmental attributes which contribute to the characteristics of 'rurality' and 'oasis'. It would be supposed that the larger the area of a green space the greater its diversity of vegetation ad the greater the possibility of retreat from the surrounding city with its traffic, noise and fumes. Thus the expectation would be that the larger the green space, the

nearer it would approach 'rural' conditions and thus provide people using it with an illusion of an oasis in the city. Possible correlations between area and four environmental factors were therefore explored for a sample of 30 green spaces within the City. The spaces were selected to represent a sample of different types and sizes. Four indices were used for each green space:

- **Rural Element Index.** This records the types of vegetation (for example grass and shrubs) and more significantly the amount of each type (the number of trees, the number of tree species and the total amount of vegetated area).

- **Urban-Rural Index.** This is an index representing the arrangement of the vegetation and how far it can produce a feeling of enclosure and 'rurality' and therefore a sense of 'oasis' in an urban environment. It is largely assessed by the ability of the trees and shrubs present to provide a screen from the surrounding buildings.

- **Environmental Index.** This is a composite index and is based on the mean score of five attributes (urban-rural; incongruous-harmonious; noisy-calm; littered-tidy; dull-attractive), two of which are considered separately here (see chapter 3).

- **Noisy-Calm Index.** This is an assessment which indicates the average noise levels experienced in each green space. In some cases the assessment has been calibrated with decibel readings (see chapter 7). The results are shown in Table 4.2.

Overall, the relationships between the four indices and area were rather weak. There was no significant relationship between either the urban-rural index or the noisy-calm index and area. The strongest relationship was found between the rural element index and area (Fig. 4.4) which had a positive linear correlation of 0.537 ($r^2 = 0.362$; $f = 18$; $p < 0.001$; $n = 30$). There was also a weaker positive linear relationship between the environmental index and area ($r^2 = 0.314$; $f = 14.7$; $p < 0.01$; $n = 30$) but visual inspection suggests that these relationships are more likely to be curved than linear.

Table 4.2 Thirty green spaces in the City of London: their areas and four indices of their 'rurality' and 'oasis' qualities, derived as described in the text.

		Area (m²)	Rural Element Index	Urban-Rural Index	Environmental Index	Noisy-Calm Index
1	Inner Temple	16879.2	12	2.0	3.6	3.0
2	Barbican (Defoe Garden)	8283.6	9	1.5	3.0	2.9
3	Finsbury Circus	7284.0	11	3.0	3.7	2.8
4	Middle Temple	4831.0	11	2.0	3.6	3.0
5	St. Paul's Churchyard	4776.7	12	3.0	3.5	2.5
6	Barbican (Farm Street)	3279.1	10	2.5	3.5	3.0
7	Info. Centre Garden (opposite St. Paul's Cath.)	2028.0	9	1.0	2.0	1.0
8	Postman's Park	1926.6	10	2.0	2.8	2.5
9	1951 Festival Garden by St. Paul's Cathedral	1825.2	10	2.0	2.5	2.0
10	St. Anne and St. Agnes Churchyard	1326.0	9	2.0	2.8	2.0
11	St. Botolph's-without-Bishopsgate Churchyard	1238.6	8	4.0	3.1	2.5
12	Newgate Street	1092.0	9	2.0	2.4	2.0
13	Bread Street Garden	1045.2	5	2.5	2.5	2.0
14	Holborn Circus Green Space	867.4	10	3.0	3.0	1.0
15	Noble Street	858.0	5	2.0	2.5	3.0
16	Cannon Street (Gateway House)	780.0	9	2.5	3.0	1.5
17	St. Paul's West Churchyard	712.9	8	1.0	2.3	1.0
18	Goldsmith's Garden	686.4	5	1.5	2.3	2.0
19	St. Michael, Cornhill Churchyard	652.1	7	3.5	2.9	3.5
20	Snow Hill Court	591.2	7	3.5	3.9	4.0
21	Remington House Garden	429.0	4	2.0	2.7	1.0
22	St. Andrew's Church	360.4	7	2.0	2.8	2.0
23	St. Mary Staining	351.0	8	1.5	2.6	3.0
24	Police Section House Garden	240.2	9	2.0	2.8	4.0
25	Holborn Viaduct/ Charterhouse Street Garden	229.3	10	1.0	2.6	1.0
26	Harrow Place Garden (Cutlers Court)	174.7	8	3.0	3.4	4.0
27	St. Andrew-by-the-Wardrobe	149.8	10	2.0	1.8	1.0
28	Holy Sepulchre Forecourt	74.9	8	3.0	3.0	2.0
29	Bank of England Garden	62.4	7	1.5	3.2	4.0
30	Dutch Church, Austin Friars Green Space	53.0	5	1.5	2.8	3.5

This is interesting in that it suggests that these indices increase rapidly as the area of small spaces increases, but much more slowly above an area of about 5,000 m².

Further correlations were computed between those indices which were thought most likely to show a relationship; for example, there was a correlation of 0.25 between the urban-rural index and the noisy-calm index. However, these relationships were found to be insignificant.

It is not unexpected that the strongest correlation was

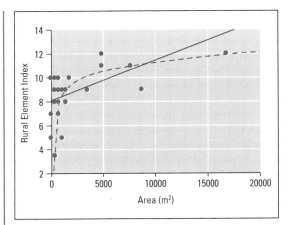

Figure 4.4   The relationship between the Rural Element Index (calculated as in Table 3.2) and area of the green spaces in the City of London.

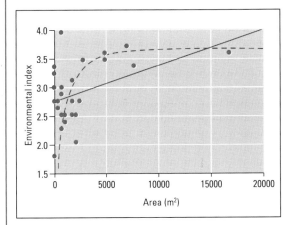

Figure 4.5   Relationship between the Environmental Index (calculated as the Design and Aesthetic Rating in Table 3.1) and area of green spaces in the City of London. (Data in Table 4.2; statistics in text.)

found between area and the rural element index since the larger a green space is, the more types of rural element (shrubs and trees) and number it can include within its boundaries. However, there are a large proportion of notable exceptions. For example, Bread Street Garden (see Table 4.2), with a reasonably large area of 1,045.2 m², has a low rural element index of 5, while St. Andrew-by-the-Wardrobe, with a small area of 149.8 m², has a relatively high rural element index of 10. This illustrates that design is all important and

that even small-sized green spaces can accommodate numerous rural elements in some abundance. Similarly, Holy Sepulchre Forecourt, with a minute area of 74.9 m², attains a rural element index of 8, the same score as St. Botolph's-without-Bishopsgate Churchyard, with a much larger area of 1,238.6 m². Many high rural element index values recorded for the smaller areas can possibly be explained by the fact that the index is weighted in favour of the smaller areas. Consequently, a score of 3 for the number of trees above 10 (see Appendix) within any area remains constant whilst the number of species recorded also works in favour of smaller areas. Similarly, larger green spaces tend to have a smaller percentage of their total area vegetated while the reverse is true for smaller spaces.

For large areas with a high rural element index there is not necessarily a correspondingly high urban-rural index. For example, a high rural element index of 10 for the 1951 Festival Garden by St. Paul's Cathedral (area 1,825.2 m²) is only accorded an urban-rural index of 2.0. This suggests that there is no relationship between abundance and arrangement of vegetation as an urban screen within the City's green spaces. Thus, although certain areas may have many rural elements in abundance, this does not necessarily create a feeling of 'rural' enclosure or 'oasis'.

There was no realistic correlation between area and the urban-rural index, with smaller green spaces such as Snow Hill Court (area 591.2 m²) and St. Michael, Cornhill (area 652.1 m²) both obtaining an urban-rural index of 3.5. However, the Information Centre Garden opposite St. Paul's Cathedral (area 2,028.0 m²) and the Barbican (Defoe Garden) green space (area 8,283.6m²) obtained scores of 1.0 and 1.5 respectively. This suggests that each green space's urban-rural index depends as much on the individual site and planting arrangements as on area. For example, Snow Hill Court is perceived as a quiet 'oasis', whereas the 'open' design of the Information Centre Garden permits considerable urban intrusion, especially due to its position alongside the busy road of St Paul's Churchyard leading to Cannon Street.

The environmental index, giving an idea of the overall ambience of each green space, shows only a weak correlation with area. For instance, the miniature Bank of England garden, with an area of 62.4 m², has an environmental index of 3.2, compared to only 2.8 for Postman's Park, with a much larger area of 1,926.6 m². The highest environmental index did not belong to the largest green space (the Inner Temple Garden, with an area of 16,879.2 m²) as might be expected, but to Snow Hill Court, twentieth in the size rankings for the green space sample.

Nevertheless, within the densely built-up City, a larger green space would be more noticeable and therefore probably more appealing than a smaller one. The environmental index also includes factors of harmony (fitting in with surroundings) and attractiveness (see survey methods) which, although these are not normally associated with area, may influence the way in which a green space is perceived.

No valid correlation was found between area and the noisy-calm index. Whether a green space is noisy or calm depends almost entirely on its location in relation to the main traffic arteries. Thus, the high calmness experienced at Harrow Place Garden (Cutlers' Court) (area 174.7 m²; noisy-calm index 4.0) is due to the surrounding buildings acting as an aural buffer from the heavy traffic noises. This can be contrasted with the very high noise levels experienced at the larger Holborn Circus green space (area 867.4 m²; noisy-calm index 1.0) which is due to the fact that it lies on a busy City 'secondary' routeway (Corporation of London 1984). However, in very large green spaces, area can influence noise levels. Within the Inner Temple Garden, different noisy-calm indices were recorded, with the noise being very much diminished away from Victoria Embankment (for the

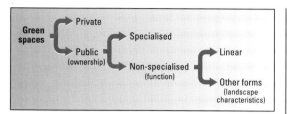

Figure 4.6   A schematic representation of the classification devised by Coronio & Muret (1976) for open spaces.

purposes of correlation, though, an average index had to be used for calculation).

*   *   *   *   *

Overall, no very firm correlation patterns or relationships emerged and it can therefore be concluded that the variation in the area of the City's green spaces does not necessarily determine the 'rurality' each exhibits. It is therefore suggested that management policy has, inadvertently, a large influence in determining the rural character – the rurality – of a green space. However, with so many low indices of 'rurality' recorded (see Table 4.2), it is clear that there are too few green 'oases' within the City. More green areas, especially those away from the major traffic arteries, should be managed with the specific intention of creating and sustaining tranquil 'oases' for people who work within the City.

The open spaces of the City illustrate a diversity of 'open-scape' types. However, a major problem lies in how best to register their distinctiveness. There are three possible ways: by ownership, by function, and by the

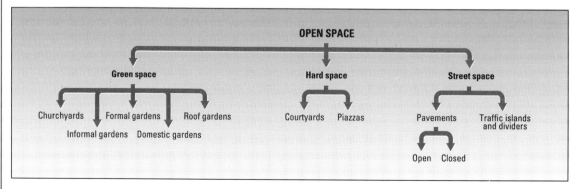

Figure 4.7   The Classification of open spaces based on landscape characteristics as used in this study.

dominant landscape characteristics of the space. A system devised by Coronio and Muret (1976) incorporates all three of these elements (see Fig. 4.6). Although the system is intended for much larger areas than the City, it is a useful guide to follow.

City open spaces are held under various types of ownership, with different degrees of public access; however, a classification based solely on these factors is not very useful. There is no relationship between ownership and land use in the City's open spaces so that, although a division based on ownership could be made, their visual appearance will not be related to ownership.

Similarly, a classification of open spaces on a functional basis would not work as all fulfil a recreational role whether on a purely visual basis or by providing space and facilities for rest and recreation. However, if open spaces are classified according to their dominant 'landscape' characteristics, the categorization, while obviously subjective, is useful because the resulting typology can be easily recognised. The system used is presented in Fig. 4.7. In all, nine distinctive types of open space may be recognised in the City, and are briefly discussed below.

This system allows for flexibility in classifying spaces; for example, the term 'square' could be used as a distinct category of open space, but on closer examination the few squares in the City are of very different character and are linked only by name. Aldermanbury Square has the characteristics of a formally laid out traffic island, and is very small (306 m^2), Devonshire Square, although basically a traffic island, is of a completely different character since its redevelopment. It would be wrong to include such examples in the same category and so the *dominant open space features* are used as the basis for their characterisation.

Green Space

Churchyards

These fall into two distinct categories: firstly, open spaces which are adjacent to present church buildings; and secondly, those which either include the ruins of a church or are laid out on the site of the original church and/or churchyard. A notable feature of City churchyards is their wide variation in size, ranging from under 100 m^2 to over 6,000 m^2. However, if St Paul's Churchyard (by far the largest in the City) is excluded, their mean size is 450 m^2. Even though many churchyards have been much reduced in size since their original establishment, they still account for around one quarter of the open space area of the City. As well as being the largest in the City the Churchurchyard of St Paul's Cathedral (Plate 4.1) is particularly distinguished in that it has an exceptional variety of exotic trees. The St Dunstan in the East church garden is another distinguished open space; the ruins of the church, bombed during the Second World War, have been incorporated into a well-designed garden on several levels with many intimate and 'private' areas which provide welcome escape from the busy surrounding area.

There is no 'standard' design for City churchyards, each having individual characteristics depending on the surroundings and history (see Plates 4.2 & 4.3). Nevertheless, it can be said that the following are

Plate 4.1   St. Paul's Churchyard

typical of many churchyards that lie adjacent to present church buildings: St Brides, Fleet Street; St Helen, Bishopsgate; and St Michael, Cornhill. Churchyards without churches include St Peter Cheap, at the junction of Wood Street and Cheapside; St Mary Somerset, Castle Baynard Street; and St Mary Staining.

Formal Gardens

Formal gardens can be considered as open spaces which are highly stylised, often incorporating formalistic design patterns. Within this category there is a wide variety of gardens, some emphasising rectangu-

Plate 4.2   St. Olave

Plate 4.3   St. Bartholomew-the-Great

Plate 4.4   The 1951 Festival Garden

Plate 4.5   Finsbury Circus

Plate 4.6   Girdlers' Garden

Plate 4.7   The Cleary Garden

Plate 4.8   Woodland Glade, Barbican

larity and linear features while others are more curvilinear and less apparently stylised. The 1951 Festival Gardens (Plate 4.4) emphasise a geometrical design with rows of annuals, and a well manicured central rectangular lawn. In contrast, Finsbury Circus (Plate 4.5) is less geometrical in layout even though it shows a considerable degree of formality, as can be seen in the highly organised floral displays.

The following examples exhibit many different characteristics but all contain formal design elements, and serve to show the wide variety of formal gardens: the Information Centre garden (Plate 6.5); the Seething Lane garden (Plate 8.4); the garden of the Bank of England; and the Salters' Garden (Plate 5.11).

Country House Gardens

There are a few open spaces which exhibit the rich informality often associated with English country houses. Probably the most notable example is the Girdlers' garden in Basinghall Avenue, which includes a patio with planters and a small mulberry tree (Plate 4.6). The intimate quality of this garden is emphasised by the monolithic high rise buildings adjacent.

Other notable examples include the Cleary Garden in Queen Victoria Street (Plate 4.7), with its pergola, which is developed on different levels because the site slopes towards the river. The gardens of the northern side of the Barbican complex present a more expansive and informal garden image, with several 'woodland glades' (Plate 4.8).

Domestic Gardens

Domestic gardens are plots for the exclusive use of individual households. The Andrewes House Gardens, the Barbican complex (Plate 4.10) and the Amen Court Garden off Warwick Lane (Plate 4.9) provide examples of this very rare type of garden in the City. The domestic nature of these gardens is well illustrated at Amen Court where the surrounding buildings provide homes for the clergy of St Paul's Cathedral and a childrens play frame reflects practical use of the space. A further example is the Masters Garden in the Temple area.

Plate 4.9   Amen Court

Plate 4.10   Brandon Mews, Barbican

Plate 4.11   Wild Garden in the Barbican

Wild Gardens

There are no areas of native vegetation in the City and now the last wasteland site at Ludgate Hill is being developed very little if any wasteland vegetation of significance remains. However, one area on the north side of the Barbican (Plate 4.11) can be singled out as a developing wildscape.

Roof Gardens

There are a number of roof gardens in the City but no detailed investigation has been carried out. It is known, however, that some companies do maintain, or are constructing, roof gardens at present. A notable example of this type of garden is above the Guildhall School of Music and Drama, while the conservatory above the

Plate 4.12   The Barbican conservatory (Top)

Plate 4.13   Crosby Court, Bishopsgate (Left)

Barbican centre can be regarded as a special case.

Enclosed Gardens

Recently a number of business developments have included atriums within their buildings. Crosby Court in Bishopsgate (Plate 4.13) is perhaps one of the most significant examples with a vegetational display used to considerable environmental effect. There are now numerous examples, albeit on a smaller scale within the City. Sheltered entrance ways with planters are another common feature found in recent office developments.

Hard Space

Courtyards

These are usually small scale open spaces that are enclosed by buildings on at least three sides and are mostly hard surfaced. The Inns of Court (Plate 4.14) epitomise the character of courtyards, being similar to the 'close' or 'quad' of the older universities. The

Plate 4.14   Fountain Court

Plate 4.15   Cutlers Court

Plate 4.16   St. Bartholomew's Hospital

Cutlers' Court complex is a special case and includes several courtyards (Plate 4.15), laid out on a functional basis. St Bartholomews provides yet another example of a more public and open courtyard style (Plate 4.16).

Piazzas

Piazzas are similar to courtyards, being hard surfaced and surrounded by buildings, but they are generally much larger. Many courtyards are less than 350 m² in area while piazzas may be as large as 5,000 m². Probably the best known, but rather drab, example is that of Paternoster Square (Plate 4.17). Further examples are the areas to the north and south of the Guildhall (Plate 4.18), St Giles Piazza in the Barbican complex (Plate 4.19) and the hard space at the corner of St Mary Axe and Leadenhall Street.

Plate 4.17   Paternoster Square (Top right)

Plate 4.18   Guildhall Yard (Right)

Plate 4.19   St. Giles, Barbican (Bottom)

Street Gardens

Pavements

These linear features may be subdivided into:

Plate 4.20   Cheapside

Plate 4.21   Holborn Circus *c* 1969

Plate 4.22   Holborn Circus

Closed Pavements

A closed pavement represents a section of street pavement which has been adapted and enclosed so as to screen the area from passing traffic and to segregate it from pedestrian traffic movement. For instance, at Cheapside (Plate 4.20), the space is partially screened by hedges and further separated from pedestrian traffic movement by its position slightly lower than the surrounding pavement level. This type of development has been more successful with the garden at Holborn Circus (Plates 4.21 & 4.22) which attains a higher degree of visual separation from the surrounding street traffic by the successful use of trees and tall hedges.

Open Pavements

These form a continuation or an addition to the normal street pavement, set out as a recreational feature yet permitting unhindered pedestrian movement (see Plate 4.23). Austral House Place, Coleman Street,

Plate 4.23   Cutlers Court Gardens

Plate 4.24   Austral House Place

Plate 4.25   St. Lawrence Jewry-next-Guildhall

is one such space (Plate 4.24), as is Moorgate (Plate 4.28), where two adjacent flower beds, separated by a walkway lined with seating, provide a setting for public relaxation. St Vedat's Place, Foster Lane provides a further example, with seats, flower beds and three small trees. The original courtyard of St Lawrence Jewry (Plate 4.25) next to Guildhall has been encompassed within the Guildhall Piazza, however, at the west end of the church on the pavement adjacent to the junction of Gresham Street with Aldermanbury, a small pond with surrounding trees has been incorporated as an open pavement feature. Unfortunately it is not as architecturally effective as it could have been and is rather out of place in its setting.

Traffic Islands and Dividers

These are purely visual, ornamental, 'miniature' open spaces which form a part of many streetscapes. An example of successful street planters are those found on the pavement adjacent to Camomile Street (Plate 4.27) approaching Houndsditch. These beds are colourful in summer and brighten the City considerably. However, the small tree and flower bed in Houndsditch facing Camomile Street is not as successful, because, unlike the former planters, it is not raised above pavement level and is thus prone to damage by heavy pedestrian traffic and litter (Plate 4.27).

Street planters also include tubs and small containers,

Plate 4.26   Gresham Street

Plate 4.27   Houndsditch

Plate 4.28   Moorgate, London Wall

some of which can be used with great effect; however, far too many appear as 'statutory' green spots, often tending to detract from rather than enhance the landscape, as in the case of Paternoster Square. Further examples of street planters occur throughout the City, notably in Queen Victoria Street, Queen Street, Ludgate Circus, Aldgate, Ropemaker Street and Gresham Street (Plate 4.26).

Traffic islands in the City often take the form of ornamental gardens although their function as green spaces can be only visual. Notable examples include the attractive green islands at the junction of Moorgate (Plate 4.28) and London Wall, and those at the junction of Blackfriars Bridge, Queen Victoria Street and Victoria Embankment.

Conclusion

This chapter has highlighted the important role open spaces play in shaping the townscape of the City. Green spaces, hard spaces and street gardens make their own particular impact in numerous ways, from contrasting colour and texture of floorscapes and features separating traffic from pedestrians to being significant architectural features in their own right. Elements within open spaces ranging from outdoor furniture to the disposition of species of trees and shrubs can readily alter perceptions of the adjacent buildings or roads, generally for the better. The effects on the surrounding areas are numerous and range from the modification of scale (such as trees making an area look larger) to contrasts in colour and texture, and the unification of various architectural styles. The survey of street trees shows that they are often dominant architectural components, and have a wide influence on the townscape. They have great architectural impact: functioning as foils to traffic or buildings, giving the impression of greater open space, and enhancing the townscape by adding texture and colour contrasts. With present building trends favouring plain buildings, the importance of trees and open space in providing contrast is likely to increase in the future.

From the observations on 'rurality' and 'oasis' value it is clear that many of the City's open spaces do not provide the tranquility sought by many, albeit for short periods. It might be thought that the reason for this situation lies in their relatively small size and the location of particular sites, but it would appear to be rather a question of design and planting policy.

The typology of City open spaces presented emphasises the attributes rather than the name of each space, thus St Giles Cripplegate is classified as a piazza due to its large paved nature rather than as a churchyard even though the church forms the centrepiece of the space and some tombstones have been preserved. The classification uses the image of a churchyard as an enclosed, ethereal and antiquated place; St Giles could only be termed a churchyard if the paved surroundings were more sympathetic to the Church itself.

The typology is descriptive of the characteristics of each space and also provides clues to the intrinsic nature of each garden type. 'Country house garden' provides an image of an intimate, informal open space, whereas formal gardens can be expected to be more stylised and 'methodical' in their layout.

A classification of this nature cannot be 'scientifically' precise in its definition of each of the many types of open space found in the City. Indeed some of the problems facing landscape classification generally are evident here, such as the different ways in which individuals may perceive a particular open space. However, within its limits, the typology is useful as it articulates the great variety of the City's open spaces, and emphasises the importance of churchyards in providing a network of open spaces throughout the whole of the City.

St. Botolph's, Bishopsgate Churchyard

CHAPTER 5

Open Spaces for Recreation, Leisure and Tourism

The open spaces of the City have a wide range of recreational uses, ranging from the purely functional, such as use as a lunch spot, to a wider appreciation of open-space heritage, that is, use as a tourist attraction. However, the use of a space is largely dependent on the facilities offered (for instance, seating, entertainment, sports courts), the size of the area and the distance that people have to travel to use it. A degree of external organisation may add to the recreational value of open spaces (although size restrictions and a lack of facilities reduce opportunities for this in the City, exceptions being tennis and netball in St Botolph's-without-Bishopsgate Churchyard and bowling in Finsbury Circus), and the production of guidebooks to make walks more informative would no doubt add to the value of the City's green spaces.

The type of user will also affect how a space is used; an office worker may use a space for a transitory rest, near to work or shops; tourists may use the spaces for longer rests or as attractions in their own right; and the different types of space in the Barbican will be used for various activities depending on whether they are used by visitors or residents. Other factors influencing recreational use are the distance travelled by the users and the climate. Office workers may use only local spaces, as lunch-breaks may be too valuable to spend travelling (unless entertainment or other events are provided), whereas tourists and other visitors are more likely to travel further; they have more time to do so, and the opportunity to 'discover' the open spaces of the City is an added bonus when visiting major attractions. Obviously climate will be a dominant factor in patterns of open space use: the summer period will see increased use by both tourists and office workers. More detailed information on temperature considerations is presented later.

User Surveys

This chapter looks at the dominant trends in the recreational use of open spaces, the relationship between environmental factors and that use, and concludes with suggestions for widening the use of City open spaces. Four surveys were carried out to determine an overall pattern of recreational use. The first aimed to find the distribution of uses and the popularity of open spaces throughout the City.

In 1983, as part of the initial Green Space Survey, a count was made of people using the City's open spaces during lunchtime in autumn. As it was not possible to conduct an overall use survey during the summer period recourse was made to the Pedestrian Movement Survey of 1969 (Corporati of London 1970) which contained an estimate (based on interviews of people working within 'street blocks' covering the City) of the number of people likely to be using open spaces at lunchtimes in the summer. Although the number of people employed within the City fell by approximately 12% in this period (1969-1983), the number of visitors rose significantly (Corporation of London 1986).

In order to make a comparison between the two surveys they were both reduced to a common denominator – the number of people using open spaces within the Ordnance Survey grid squares covering the City. The figures given for the 1969 Survey represent only an estimate and in any case a strict numerical comparison with the 1983 Survey would be inappropriate for surveys conducted over ten years apart. Rather, the importance of the two sets of figures lies in their illustration of the overall difference shown in the magnitude of use between summer and autumn and as a guide to the overall pattern of open space use within the City. The 1969 Survey also established a hierarchy of the most frequently used open spaces in the City.

In 1985 a summer survey was made, visiting each of the open spaces identified in 1969 during the lunchtime period (12.30 to 2.00 pm and the 'rush hour' periods) and undertaking an 'on the spot' count. The 1983 and 1985 surveys were conducted within the open spaces themselves and were designed to ascertain why people used specific open spaces and what they did in them. A small sample survey was also conducted within business premises as part of the second survey. The final pilot survey was devised to determine the attitude of people in the City towards open spaces generally and was conducted by interview in City streets.

Comparative Results – 1969 and 1983

As might be expected, the results shown in Fig. 5.1 indicate that there are far more open space users in summer than in autumn. Nevertheless, the overall pattern of user distribution is similar, with the peaks and troughs largely coinciding. Generally, lower figures for both summer and autumn are recorded in grid squares which only cover a part of the City (this is particularly true for grid squares 2 and 3), and higher figures are recorded where a grid square fully covers a part of the City (for example 10 and 11).

The grid squares with the highest usage of open space remain the same for both surveys. The greatest use of open space both in summer and in autumn falls into grid squares 10, 11, 13 and 19. This is no doubt due to the fact that each of these squares contains a high

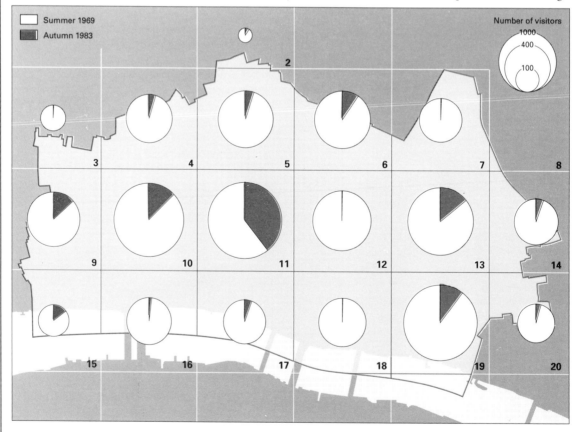

Figure 5.1   The relative numbers of open space users in different areas of the City of London (size of circle) and a comparison between numbers counted in autumn 1983 (shaded portion) and in summer 1969.

number of open spaces which appear to be much more heavily used. The high use in square 19 can partly be explained by the proximity of the Tower of London.

However, these four squares account for 74% of City open space usage in autumn as against only 43% in summer. This can partly be explained by the greater spread of summer usage in all open spaces whereas in autumn there is a tendency for open space use to be more closely related to major tourist attractions such as St Paul's Cathedral which lies in grid square 11. Indeed, this grid square accounts for 40% of total open space use in autumn but only 12% in summer.

Exceptions to the general pattern do occur. Open spaces within grid squares 7, 12 and 18 (which experience very little use in autumn), show a disproportionately high use in summer. This probably suggests that people who were interviewed within a grid square do not necessarily use the open spaces within that square either because there are too few open spaces in their immediate area or because they prefer alternative, more distant open spaces. For instance, grid square 12, despite being entirely within the City, shows a very low open space usage in autumn basically because there are only a relatively few small open spaces within that square. The very high summer results can be probably accounted for by people from square 12 using the numerous open spaces in square 11, in particular St Paul's Churchyard to the west, or some of the open space in square 6, in particular Finsbury Circus to the north.

Open space use in other grid squares is much less than might be expected. Square 20 shows a low use for both summer and autumn because the City boundaries do not include the Tower Gardens, Wakefield Gardens or the Trinity Square Gardens which are all major tourist attractions but within the London Borough of Tower Hamlets. Square 15, which mainly incorporates the large area of the Temple Gardens, has only a modest use because they are not ordinarily open to the public. The large difference between the summer and autumn open space use within square 5 can be partly explained by the likelihood that the high summer figures include the public areas of the Barbican such as St Giles' Piazza and the Barbican Centre Forecourt (Lakeside Terrace)

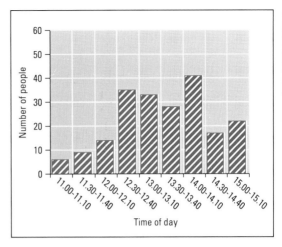

Figure 5.2 The number of people entering Finsbury Circus during the lunchtime period in late autumn.

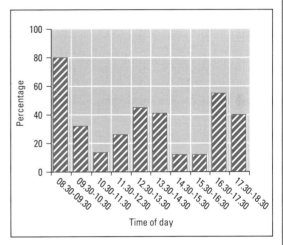

Figure 5.3 Time distribution of people walking through Paternoster Square between 08.30 and 18.30 (*n*=5000).

while the low autumn figures included only the private Barbican Gardens reserved for residents.

Comparative Results – 1969 and 1985

Table 5.1 shows that in 1969 the most popular open space was Finsbury Circus (32 per cent of open space users). In 1985 the most popular open space was Paternoster Square (26 per cent of open space users). St Paul's Churchyard was the second most frequently used open space in both cases. The least used spaces are essentially the same in both surveys. The main points to emerge from this survey are firstly that the top five entries in 1969 remain the top five in 1985 although in a slightly changed order. Secondly, these top entries accounted for some 85% of open space usage in 1969 and over 90% in 1985.

Table 5.1   The most frequently used open spaces in the 1969 and 1985 surveys (for details see text). The figures are percentages of the total number of open space users counted in each survey.

	1969*	1985
Finsbury Circus	32	16
St. Paul's Churchyard	17	22
The Inns of Court	13	12
Paternoster Square	12	26
Tower Hill	10	16**
Victoria Embankment	5	2
North of the City	4	3
Bishopsgate Churchyard		
(St. Botolph's)	4	1
Temple	3	2

*   These figures do not include the Tower of London

**   Assumed figure from initial green space survey data

Many of the larger open spaces are used throughout the year. However, on the spot observations seem to indicate that the smaller areas are relatively much less used during late autumn and winter. The large spaces lend themselves to the more active forms of recreation during the cooler seasons.

The majority of open spaces are most used during the lunch period and a typical use pattern is illustrated for Finsbury Circus during late autumn (Fig. 5.2). The pattern would largely remain the same during the summer but the total number of visitors would be very much increased. Some open spaces do show typical patterns: for instance, open spaces used as 'routeways' show morning and evening peaks as people are recorded walking through, as is the case in Paternoster Square (Fig. 5.3).

Why do people visit specific open spaces?

To identify what attracted an individual to a particular open space, a sample survey of users were asked why they visited the open space in question. The only recorded result in the 1969 survey was that approximately 30 per cent of people used a particular open space because it was convenient to their place of work; other reasons were not recorded. The 1985 survey, conducted in open spaces in the Bishopsgate-Moorgate area, also shows that the majority of respondents (62 per cent) used open spaces because they were close to their place of work. However, the survey also shows the other reasons why people use specific open spaces (see Table 5.2).

Table 5.2   Reasons given by members of the public for their use of open spaces in 1985 (n=200).

Reasons	%
Convenient for work	62
Only one known	13
Close to station	5
Entertainment	4
No reason given	4
To visit a church	4
Convenient for shops	3
Pleasant appearance	3
Freedom from traffic	2

The second most important reason (13 per cent) given for people using a particular open space indicates that it was the only one known to them. The remaining 25 per cent of respondents gave reasons that could be described largely as 'site specific'. For example, when the individual sites are examined it is found that 17 per cent of the respondents who used St Botolph's did so because it was a pleasant place to await the departure of their train from nearby Liverpool Street Station and 14 per cent of the respondents who used Finsbury Circus did so when musical entertainment was provided.

In the same area a pilot survey ($n = 25$), within business premises, of staff members using open spaces revealed a similar ranking of results to that shown in Table 5.2, the only significant difference being that 'freedom from traffic' was considered to be the third most

Plate 5.1   A break from the office

Plate 5.3   A sunshine snack

Plate 5.2   Bowls in Finsbury Circus

Plate 5.4   Lunchtime relaxation

important reason for using open spaces at lunch time.

What people do in open spaces

Table 5.3 shows the actual activities recorded within open spaces. Unfortunately, the 1969 and 1985 survey methods differed in that the 1985 survey only identified the single most important reason, whereas the 1969 survey identified more than one reason. Therefore in the 1969 survey the individual percentages total more than 100 per cent. Nevertheless, the results are comparable.

Table 5.3 Comparison of the activities of people using open spaces in 1969 and 1985 (for differences in methodology see text).

	1969	1985
Walking	54	9
Sitting	47	68
Eating	15	22
Other	2	1

As might be expected, given the generally small size of City open spaces, particularly in the central areas and lunchtime being that of peak usage, sitting and eating are major activities recorded in both surveys (Plates 5.1 – 5.5).

Obviously, the use of open space varies considerably with the weather, time of year and time of day (Figs. 5.2 and 5.3). The results in both surveys compare the midday/lunchtime use of open spaces during the summer with autumn.

General attitudes of people to City open space

This survey was conducted at various pavement locations within the Bishopsgate, Moorgate and Farringdon Street areas in 1985. Pedestrians were asked whether they used City open spaces or not and then they were asked for their reasons for using or not using open spaces. Once again, where possible, the results of this survey were compared with those of the 1969 survey (see Table 5.4).

The 71:29 per cent split between non-users and users of open space is interesting in that it is not too dissimilar to the 62:38 per cent split found in the *Pedestrian Movement Survey* of 1969 (Corporation of London 1970), indicating that the proportion of City employees, residents and visitors using open space remains at about one-third of the daytime population. This would tend to confirm the conclusion reached in the City of London Development Plan Background Study (Corporation of London 1978c), indicating only a minority use of City open spaces, albeit a large minority.

The results of the second question again correspond in large measure with the reasons given in the 1969 survey

(Table 5.4). For instance, lack of time and lack of knowledge of open spaces in existence were the reasons given most frequently. Two per cent had a general antipathy to using these areas because of the general unpleasantness of the environment. (For instance, the presence of vagrants or where carbon monoxide and noise pollution reached undesirable levels.) Although the percentage figures for other reasons are low, they are of significance for the management planning and design of open spaces.

Table 5.4 The percentage of persons using/not using open spaces in the City and the reasons given in 1985 for not using open spaces (*n*=100).

	1969 survey	1985 survey
Respondents who use open space	38	29
Respondents who do not use open space	62	71

Why not?	
Lack of time	43%
Lacked knowledge of existence of open spaces	15%
Too far from workplace	4%
Prefer public houses/restaurants	4%
Passing through	3%
Environmental unpleasantness	2%

Plate 5.5 Broadgate

The relatively high percentage recorded for those who do not realise that open spaces may be found close to their places of work is suprising. Certainly if many of the people represented by this percentage were to use nearby open spaces it is possible to argue that the overall use (at lunchtime) of open spaces would be considerably increased.

Those people not using open spaces were also asked whether they would object to the loss of such areas to building developments. Fifty-three per cent answered that they would object to such a loss.

*   *   *   *   *

Despite survey limitations it can be stated that open spaces within the City are used by office workers and others as generally pleasant places within which to eat and relax at lunchtime. There is some evidence to suggest that open spaces, especially within the central areas of the City, are insufficient in size and number to cope with the peak summer lunchtime demand. From information on the numbers of workers in the City the amount of open space per worker was calculated. This is 0.29 m^2 per person in the core area (squares 11, 12, 13) and 1.12 m^2 per person for the periphery. This difference is due to both the greater density of offices in the core, and the smaller number of open spaces (and their smaller size). Thus, if demand for recreational open space is constant throughout the whole of the City, the pressures on open spaces generally will be much greater on those situated in the core. Much evidence of overcrowding can be observed during the peak period, with all seats being occupied and many people found sitting on the ground or walls and ledges, in extreme cases causing difficulty for pedestrian movement. Added to this is the possibility that should the existence and location of the present relatively small number of open spaces be better known, overcrowding could well become more acute. This situation was also noted in the Background Study (Corporation of London 1978c). Conversely, there are a small number of open spaces in the inner areas of the City which can be described as under-used at present.

One of the most important findings of the 1985 survey of general attitudes was a clear indication from non

users of open spaces that they would oppose any threats to the loss of existing open space within the City from building. This points to the evident importance people attach to open spaces in the City as an integral part of the townscape and as having psycho-aesthetic value, as well as the more utilitarian value people adduce to the City's open spaces.

The use of open spaces for tourism will now be examined, and the more structured approach to green space use mentioned in the introduction is emphasised by the inclusion of descriptions of two green trails.

City Open Spaces and Tourism

The City as the traditional heart of London has much to offer the tourist. There are the major tourist attractions such as St Paul's Cathedral, the Barbican Centre, the Museum of London and the Tower of London, which lies just outside the City boundary (see Corporation of London 1986). There are also many other attractions including historic streets and churches, the Guildhall, the Inns of Court, the Inner Temple (Plate 5.6), the Monument, sections of the old City walls and many innovative modern buildings, such as Standard Chartered Bank, Bishopsgate. However, it is frequently overlooked that many of these sites are often associated with gardens and green spaces which are attractive features in their own right. Indeed, one of the delights which awaits the tourist is to discover the many secret gardens (Boardman 1982), and the not so secret, large and small, formal and informal, open spaces which exist within the City's boundary.

Plate 5.6   Inner Temple Garden

Table 5.5 The environmental scores of green spaces included in the two green trails described in the text and illustrated in Figs. 5.5 and 5.6.

	Green Trail 1 St. Paul's Cathedral to the Barbican Centre			Green Trail 2 Barbican Centre to Liverpool St. Station	
Green Space Site Number (map and graph)	Green Space Name	Mean Score	Green Space Site Number (map and graph)	Green Space Name	Mean Score
1	1951 Festival Gardens	2.5	1	Lakeside Terrace	2.5
2	St. Paul's Churchyard	3.5	2	Lakeside Gardens	3.7
3	Cheapside	2.4	3	Andrewes House Gardens	3.4
4	St. Vedast's Place	1.8	4	Wallside	3.2
5	Postman's Park	2.8	5	St. Alphage Place	2.6
6	Goldsmiths' Garden	2.3	6	Salters' Garden	3.2
7	St. Anne & St. Agnes	2.8	7	Guildhall Piazza	2.5
8	Noble Street Gardens	2.5	8	Girdlers' Gardens	3.5
9	St. Olave's	3.3	9	Austral House Place	2.5
10	St. Mary Staining	2.6	10	Moorgate (includes three sites)	2.3
11	St. Mary Aldermanbury	3.2	11	Finsbury Circus	3.7
12	Aldermanbury Square	2.5	12	Winchester Corner	2.3
13	Brewers' Place	2.2	13	All Hallows on the Wall	2.2
14	Salters' Garden	3.2	14	St. Botlph's-without- Bishopsgate Churchyard	2.6
15	St. Alphage Place	2.6	15	Cutlers' Court	3.5
16	Monkwell Square	2.8	16	Devonshire Square	2.9
17	Wallside	3.2			
18	Andrewes House Gardens	3.4			
19	Lakeside Gardens	3.7			
20	Lakeside Terrace	2.5			

Trail No. 1 Mean Environmental Score = 2.8   Trail No. 2 Mean Environmental Score = 2.9
City Mean Environmental Score = 2.6

Plate 5.7   St. Paul's Churchyard

In order to illustrate the tourist opportunities offered by the City's green spaces two green trails have been devised (see page 65). The first of these links two major attractions, St Paul's Cathedral (Plates 5.7 & 5.8) and the Barbican Centre, and a main line terminal, Liverpool Street Station, which is a major point of access for many City visitors. These trails have also been designed to appeal not only to those who admire gardens but to the more adventurous and to 'second time' visitors and so in a small way to lessen pressure on the more congested tourist areas by encouraging people to explore some of the City's lesser known green attractions.

Plate 5.8   Old Change Court

The pilot trails introduced here present only a basic foundation from which tourist green trail leaflets should be developed and published. They are examples of a number which could be designed and two further suggestions can be mentioned: St Paul's to the Temple courts and gardens and another around the Tower which would include such sites as Seething Gardens and the magnificent garden developed on the site, and incorporating the ruins of St Dunstan-in-the-East, off St Dunstan's Hill.

In devising the trails four objectives have been kept in mind;

- to provide pleasant yet practicable green walks between major tourist attractions and access points;

- to illustrate something of the rich diversity of green space which can be found in the City;

- to include larger green areas open to the public where tourists can rest and relax;

- to give some indication of points of general and historical interest to tourists.

In this book notes are given on each green space regarding its design and layout but instructions for getting from one to the next (which would be included in a leaflet) are omitted.

It is presumed that most people who wish to follow the trails will find green spaces to be pleasant features of the City's townscape. To see whether such a presumption is true, and the degree to which it is true, a survey incorporating an assessment of 'pleasantness' was undertaken. This was based on the architecture and design of spaces, their environmental and vegetational quality and their standard of management, though not referring specifically to their heritage or amenity value as such. The assessment is based on differential semantic scales of 1-5 (the higher the score the more pleasant the attribute). The scores for each attribute for each green space were then averaged and ranked using descriptive categories ranging from 'undistinguished' to 'distinguished'. Although the method used is subjective and records only one individual's assessment of each attribute within a particular green space, at one point, and at a specific time, nevertheless its simplicity has resulted in surveyors achieving a high degree of comparability at one site and between sites. It appears that the mean score gives a fair representation of the environmental merits of each green space and thus a shorthand way of recording and ranking 'pleasantness' in the context of the City's green spaces, and gives an indication of those green spaces of particular merit along the route of the trails.

Table 5.5 illustrates the mean 'environmental' or pleasantness scores which were recorded for the open spaces visited on the two green trails. It can be seen that these scores are both above that registered for all the open spaces within the City, 61% having a higher environmental score than the City as a whole. The relative ranking of these spaces can be seen in Fig. 5.4, which shows that over 80% of these green spaces fall into the top three categories and are perceived as being

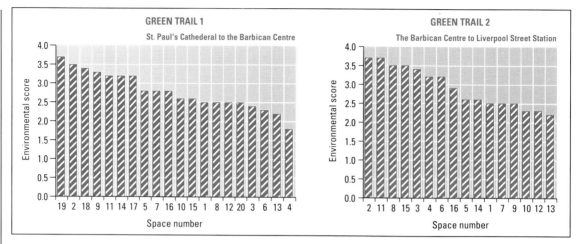

Figure 5.4   Green spaces included in the green trails ranked on the basis of their environmental scores, derived as the Design and Aesthetic rating in Table 3.1. The spaces and their scores are listed in Table 5.5.

either pleasant, attractive or, in the case of 16%, distinguished.

The highest scoring or 'most distinguished' green space of these two trails are the Lakeside Gardens of the Barbican and Finsbury Circus. Both were judged to fit harmoniously into their immediate surroundings; both evidenced a very high standard of maintenance and green space management. Lakeside Gardens were judged to be extremely attractive in an environment which largely excluded unpleasant noise. In the case of Finsbury Circus the creation of a sense of oasis and the visual exclusion, certainly in summer, of the surrounding urban environment produced a high score for this attribute. Both probably benefit in their scores because of the overall sense of space. Apart from the Temple Gardens, Finsbury Circus is one of the largest City green spaces, while an expansiveness is created by the water area and gardens beyond in the case of the Barbican Lakeside Gardens.

Other 'distinguished' green spaces on the Trails are: St Paul's Churchyard, Cutlers' Court and Girdlers' Garden. A common theme running through each of these very different green spaces is their high standard of maintenance and management.

St Paul's Churchyard, with its rather pleasing informal arrangement together with its several large trees, presents a contrasting yet harmonious setting for the building itself. Also, much of the urban scene is excluded from these gardens. In the case of Cutlers' Court there is a certain appeal in the functional way in which these 'courts' have been laid out and the overall effect, probably enhanced by its novelty and attention to detail, is judged to be attractive while many of the courtyards are reasonably calm. The high design score is also linked to the effective use and varied design of the large street planters which 'enclose' the site from the street. The Girdlers' Gardens provide an illustration of how a small garden can also be distinguished and is a good example of the fine gardening traditions of many of the City's Livery Companies.

As can be seen from Table 5.5 and from Fig. 5.4, 8 gardens are rated as 'attractive'. One which is recorded only as pleasant is that of the churchyard of St Botolph's-without-Bishopsgate. In this instance the mean score represents an assessment of the whole area including the tennis courts and other 'hard' areas, thus making it lower than might have been expected given the varied and attractive small gardens forming this green space.

The scores for individual attributes may well be increased or decreased by factors peculiar to their location. For example, the Barbican green spaces have relatively high scores in part attributed to the low noise levels compared to other green spaces in the City, while St Olave's (9) would have probably reached the 'distinguished' category had it not been for the noise generated by traffic on London Wall.

At the other end of the scale the explanation of the 'less' pleasant green spaces which fall below the City mean usually lies in the fact that they provide little in the way of a foil, either visually or aurally, to the surrounding urban environment. In a few cases, for instance Cheapside, they are less well managed. Some spaces are so much used that maintenance appears to be at a lower level.

In conclusion it can be stated that most green spaces, both in the City generally and those mentioned specifically in these two trails, conform to a high standard and add immeasurably to the City's townscape.

City Green Trails

Barbican Centre to Liverpool Street Station

The trail begins at the Barbican Centre (see Fig. 5.5), which is close to a number of underground stations and bus routes. The whole area now occupied by the Barbican was laid waste in the Second World War which provided the Corporation with an opportunity to create a comprehensive residential development to which were added other buildings, including a concert hall, to serve a wider public. The Barbican, designed by Chamberlain, Powell and Barr, has been described as one of the boldest and most imaginative examples of post-war reconstruction in Britain. (France 1974) Although the complicated layout and massive rectangularity have been much criticised, the green spaces and lakes within and adjacent to the complex considerably soften and humanise the overall stark image. This softening has become more effective as the buildings weather and as the many private and semi-public gardens have developed, with trees growing to maturity and gradually seeming to expand these green spaces, enabling them to contribute more significantly to the Barbican's overall architecture.

Leaving the Barbican Centre by the exit under the Conservatory in the direction of London Wall and crossing the bridge over the lake the first view is the (1)

Lakeside Terrace on the right (Plate 5.9). Each side of the lake is dominated by brick paving which has been employed extensively. To the left St Giles can be seen set in a 'sea' of brick while to the right is the frontage of the Barbican Centre itself (Plate 5.10). The wide terrace, with numerous tables and chairs in summer, is used by the patrons of the restaurant and snack bar. The lakeside fountains, together with planters with shrubs and small trees, go some way towards diminishing what has been described as the monotonous effect of the brick paving (France 1979) and the inappropriate scatter of tub plantings.

On the other side of the bridge are the (2) *Lakeside Gardens*. The rectangular lake, well stocked with carp, dominates the scene. Adjacent to the gardens, and adjoining the main Barbican Centre, is a brick floored terrace with seating. Overall, the effect is enhanced by the rows of window boxes which some people have rather affectionately compared to the Hanging Gardens of Babylon.

On the same level (3) *Andrewes House Gardens* can be viewed from the Postern. These small individual plots are pleasantly separated and partially screened from Fore Street by a surround of shrubs and trees.

Proceeding from the junction of the Postern with Wallside and facing the tower of St Giles Cripplegate is a very pleasant view to (4) *Wallside* open space. A grassed area with a path flanks the building. In places the remains of the City Wall and corner bastion separate the grass from the rectangular lake – a pleasant feature with aquatic plants such as reeds and water lilies provides a good and largely undisturbed habitat for a number of birds.

(5) *St Alphage Place* is a small green space with two grassed areas, a magnolia tree on one and an oak on the other. The area is enclosed from the street by a beech hedge and bounded by the City Wall (see plaque no. 12) which separates this area from (6) *The Salters' Garden* (Plate 5.11). This is entered by descending steps and passing through a delightful garden annexe, a small paved area with a banked shrub and brilliant flower bed below the road and with creepers overhanging the boundary wall. The Salters' Building itself,

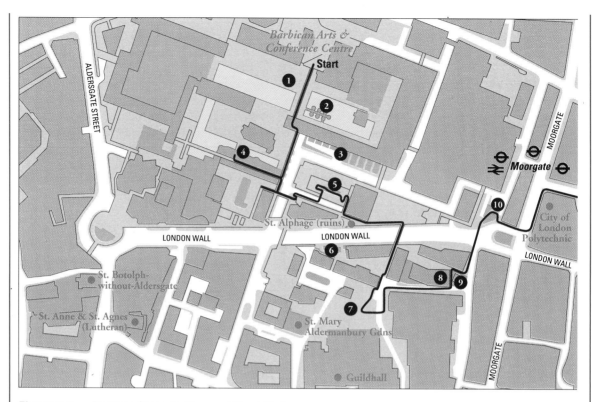

Figure 5.5   Barbican Centre to Liverpool Street Station

which occupies the site of the house of the first Lord Mayor, well offsets a remarkable section of the City Wall which forms the boundary of this garden on the opposite side. (It is Corporation policy to preserve such important archaeological remains (Corporation of London 1986).) The garden landscape is completed by some well stocked planters with palms, and seating is provided.

The (7) *Guildhall Piazza* is backed by the Civil offices and built on the site of St Michael's Church which was demolished in 1900. Even with some attempt at floorspace design, the steps and stairway planters to Bassinghall Street, with their two trees and the curved stairway feature towards Aldermanbury, this open space is rather nondescript and vacuous, enhanced only by the Glass Fountain and the sculptured figures – 'Beyond Tomorrow' – by the Swedish sculptress Karin Jonzen.

From Basinghall Avenue the extremely well kept 'country house' (8) *Girdlers' Gardens* can be seen. (9) *Austral Place* (also known as Girdlers' Hall Place) is a paved area with a large raised planter. The central planter is well stocked with a variety of shrubs, providing an attractive habitat for birds, and with planes and false acacia. It is fronted by smaller flower planters.

(10) *Moorfields Place* takes its name from the wet moor on swampy ground which was found immediately north of the City wall in this vicinity. It was eventually drained in the sixteenth and seventeenth centuries. Today this land space can be described as an informal pedestrianised area where the Moorfields and London Wall roads previously joined. The main features are two triangular and well-stocked flower/shrub planters which provide a colourful summer display separated by a pathway which is lined with a number of seats.

(11) *Finsbury Circus* is the largest of the City's public open spaces. The present Circus began life as the City's answer to the upmarket Georgian housing develop-

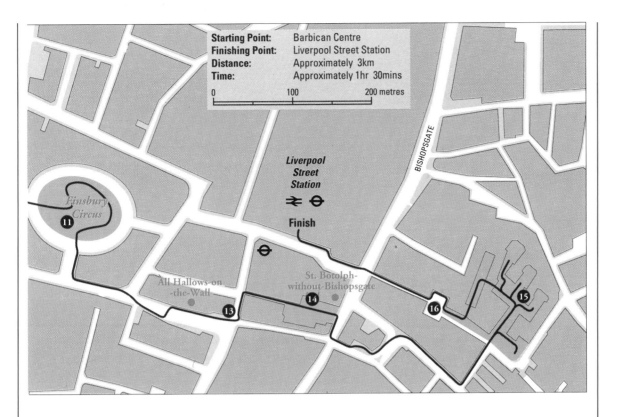

Starting Point: Barbican Centre
Finishing Point: Liverpool Street Station
Distance: Approximately 3km
Time: Approximately 1hr 30mins

0   100   200 metres

Liverpool
Street
Station

Finish

Finsbury
Circus

BISHOPSGATE

All Hallows-on
-the-Wall

St. Botolph-
without-Bishopsgate

Plate 5.9

Lakeside Terrace,
Barbican.

Plate 5.10 St. Giles Cripplegate, Barbican.

ments of the West End. The original buildings surrounding the green area have subsequently been replaced by more massive structures, which still compliment the character of the central garden. The green space itself was taken over by the Corporation of London in 1900 and has since been managed for the benefit of the general public. The garden itself is enclosed by railings and the boundary is largely encompassed by an open shrubbery with trees and planting beds. Especially noteworthy are the large mature planes which characterise the area. They give contrasting patterns of light and shade over much of this space through the seasons and also provide a much needed large scale green foil against the massive buildings surrounding the circus and in some measure contribute to a lowering of the noise level within the garden.

The central area within the surrounding path comprises four main features: the Bandstand which is used for summer concerts; the bowling green which occupies much of the central area; an architecturally undis-

tinguished Pavillion; and a most effective gently sloping grassed area with formal flower beds in the French manner. Further grassed areas and flower beds, together with a small gazebo and newly installed chess tables, complete the scene. The design and management of the area have changed over the years. For instance, the bowling green was established in 1925 and extended in 1968 (Cleary 1982) and mulberries were still being harvested in the Twenties.

(12) *Winchester Corner* is a small but effective hard surfaced open space occupying a street corner site. Across the road is the old churchyard of (13) *All Hallows-on-the-Wall*. This churchyard, which is shaded by four mature planes, is a small inset off the present street and consists of a paved area, raised above street level, which adjoins 'the rear elevation of New Broad Street and a fragment of the City Wall' (Lloyd, 1979 and City wall plaque no.10).

From Old Broad Street, Bishopsgate Churchyard is on

Plate 5.11   Salters' Garden.

the right. The hard open space flanking Broad Street House is enlivened by the exotic building which houses the Gallipoli Restaurant. The (14) *Churchyard of St. Botolph-Without-Bishopsgate* was first laid out as a public garden after the passing of the 1855 Burial Act. The small buildings, in keeping with the feeling of intimacy and which front Wormwood Street, form the churchyard boundary against which numerous shrubs and trees have been planted. In a secluded position there is a flower garden with a backdrop of shrubs. A fountain was added by the Corporation in 1972 (Cleary 1982). The church was first consecrated in 1212 and John Keats was christened in the present building in 1795.

Effective island and street planters can be observed in following Outwich Street to the junction with Houndsditch. (15) *Cutlers' Court*. The Cutler Street Warehouse complex is a site of particular townscape character (Plate 5.12). As the use for warehouses of this nature has all but disappeared in the City of today there

was considerable pressure for their demolition and for a totally new and large scale redevelopment of the area. However, a compromise solution, which has allowed some redevelopment along with the refurbishment and conversion of the warehouses for office use, has been carried out. While it can be argued that the result is not entirely successful architecturally and environmentally, it has resulted in the preservation of buildings of character and historical content. Further, it has embellished the site with linear street gardens along the Cutler Street and Devonshire Square frontage and provided a number of courts, open spaces and small gardens, open to the public and in some cases provided with seating, within.

Entering through the gateway provides the main access to the courts. The floorscape comprises small 'cobble' sets laid in a fan-shaped motif. The court is lined with miniature hornbeam planted in slightly raised small square beds covered with ivy. This court merges into a central, pivotal open area for deliveries and service.

Plate 5.12   Cutlers Court

Here there is a slightly raised grassed area and plane trees which help to relieve the bland, heavy, flat-faced buildings which enclose the central courtyard. A major feature, against shrub planters in one of the courts, is a global fountain, with the sound of its falling water counteracting less attractive city noises. Passing under the arch to the left (see Fig. 5.5) one enters West Court. This stylised court has a floorscape largely dominated by cobble sets within which, looking to the right, are small grassed areas, ground level flower beds and a number of limes set in ivy-covered beds. Benches, shrubs and laurels in tubs surround the enclosing wall.

The complex central feature includes a fountain at the south end which has an airfall, to a small pool with six illuminated miniature fountains. These water features are complemented by flower beds, slightly raised box hedged rose beds, and laurel trees.

From West Court, walking through the covered way brings one to (16) *Devonshire Square,* which was one of the City's residential developments in the mid-eighteenth century. The square is no longer 'sylvan', however and a new street garden has been built in the form of a central 'roundabout' consisting of planters with flowers, shrubs and small trees separated by diagonal walkways. On the north side of the Square four young plane trees have been planted. Coopers Hall gives some idea of the original buildings which surrounded this square (Lloyd 1979).

Devonshire Row is an intimate passageway consisting of small scale 'domestic buildings with shops below', which leads to Bishopsgate and Liverpool Street Station, where this walk ends.

St Paul's Cathedral to the Barbican Centre

The trail begins at the (1) *Festival Gardens* (Plate 4.4) adjacent to Cannon Street and St Paul's Cathedral. This green space is formally laid out with a central grassed area surrounded by a flower bed with a very colourful display of summer annuals. The centrepiece is surrounded by a paved surface at a slightly higher level. The area is well furnished with park benches and is itself seasonally enclosed by a lime hedge along Cannon Street with additional shrubs and trees. The two sections are separated by the path surrounding the centrally grassed area. Below the path are the notable wall fountains donated by the Worshipful Company of Gardeners of London who have been much concerned, as their name suggests, in maintaining a green city since the twelfth century (White 1984). These gardens are used frequently by the public, especially at lunchtime during fine summer weather.

(2) *St Paul's Churchyard.* This present green space has its origin in an agreement between the Corporation of London and the Cathedral authorities to develop the area as an open space for public amenity and it was enlarged in 1966 at the time of the building of the present Choir School (see plaque). It is sympathetically but informally laid out and much of the area is pleasantly shaded by fine mature plane trees. Florally the Churchyard is a miniature arboretum with a variety of trees including a ginkgo, one of the oldest living orders of tree with a fossil record of some 250 million years. As well as the London plane the trees include maple, lime, ash, mulberry (previously found on many city sites) and eucalyptus. The forward looking management of this area is shown by the number of saplings and young trees, which will ensure a continuing tree presence well into the future. On the north side of the green space the Victorian St Paul's cross is a significant feature. Past associations have been far from pleasant, indeed the area nearby was previously used for the execution of martyrs and Gunpowder Plot conspirators (see Weinreb and Hibbert 1983). Plaques provide more historical information while many of the trees display name plates.

Crossing New Change past the pleasing street garden flower bed outside the Bank of Boston, leads to (3)

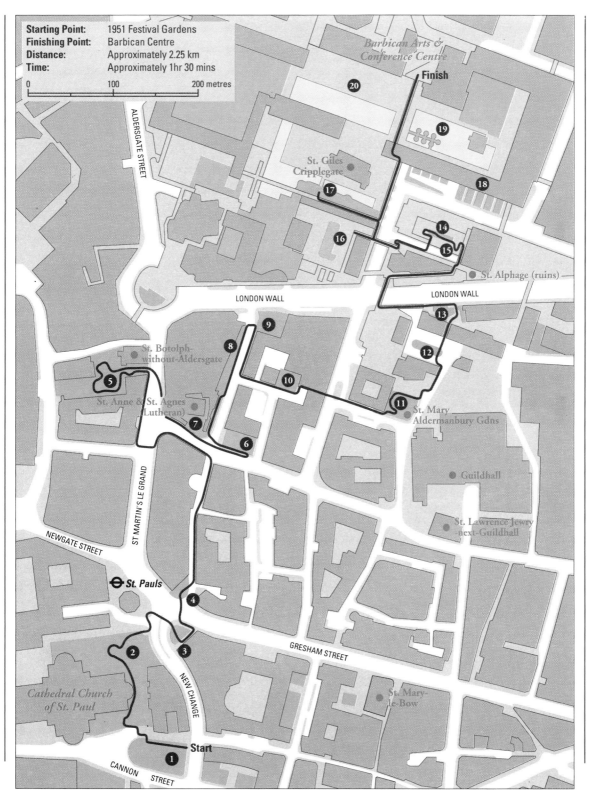

Starting Point: 1951 Festival Gardens
Finishing Point: Barbican Centre
Distance: Approximately 2.25 km
Time: Approximately 1hr 30 mins

0   100   200 metres

Figure 5.6   St. Paul's Cathedral to the Barbican Centre

Plate 5.13   Postman's Park

Cheapside. This is a land space area slightly below pavement level at the junction of New Change and Cheapside, which, despite its position beside heavily trafficked roads, (Transport and Environment Studies 1985) presents an intimate aspect. The area is encompassed by a beech hedge with openings for access from the pavement surrounding but which nevertheless provides a reasonable screen from passing traffic in summer. There are two trees and a colourful raised flower bed forming a border to part of this space. Public seating is provided while the adjoining wine bar sets out tables and chairs for its customers during the summer.

(4) *Vedast Place* is an unobtrusive open area which is really a continuation of the street pavement. Gresham Street, with some sympathetic building restoration, maintains some of its original intimate appeal. On rounding the bend in Foster Lane, Goldsmith's Hall, built between 1829 and 1835, can be seen on the right and there is a green panorama ahead with a view of the Barbican.

(5) *Postman's Park:* This green space is one of the largest in the City (approximately 2,800 m²). It is partly surrounded by the heavy architecture of the Edwardian post office building which imparts a rather sombre atmosphere (Plate 5.13). However, visitors can appreciate the relative tranquility of the park, indeed the noise levels recorded here (Table 7.6) are lower than those recorded for may other open spaces in the City. There are grassed areas, a raised shrubbery and colourful flower beds. The whole is dominated by a number of mature trees: plane, chestnut, lime, fig and black poplar. A commemorative oak was planted in 1973 to celebrate the issue of the first British stamp to bear a tree. It has now been replaced after the original was blown over in the hurricane of October 1987. There are a number of interesting monuments. Note the fountain and pool at the entrance, and the statue of the minotaur by Michael Ayrton. The effect of tranquility and sanctuary is heightened by Watt's memorial of enamel tiles (1900) to those who died sacrificing their lives for others (see White 1984).

Plate 5.14   Plaisterer's Garden

The route is retraceed to St Martin's Le Grand, Gresham Street, and Foster Lane to the Goldsmith's Hall and into (6) *Goldsmith's Garden*. This was created in its present form after the Second World War from an amalgamation of the Churchyard of St John Zachary (the church was originally destroyed in the Great Fire of 1666) and the adjoining Goldsmith's property which had been devastated by bombing. The present green space consists of one section raised above street level, a grassed area incorporating tombs from St John Zachary and dominated by two large planes. The other section has been excavated below street level and consists of a central grassed area with a hard surfaced surround with public seating arranged against the retaining wall. The space itself is simple and effectively separates these areas from Gresham Street itself.

The (7) *Churchyard of St Anne and St Agnes*. A shrub hedge with trees partially screens the area from Noble Street and produces a sense of enclosure generally and especially at the southern end with a small area of more intimate design. Another separate small grassed area with trees and shrubs bordering the pavement provides a pleasant approach to the Church itself. A variety of trees have been used in this space including maple, lime, catalpa, false acacia, plane, ash, rowan and cherry. This creates a sense of space within a small area and forms canopies of varying shapes and colour contrasts as well as providing a dapple ground shade in summer and filigree designs in winter. The ancient City Wall runs parallel with Noble Street and before leaving St Anne's and St Agnes' visitors should read the tiled notice – panel 20 – which relates to the history of the Wall.

Proceeding along Noble Street towards London Wall, the trail passes (8) *Wall Green*. This is an elongated strip of green space, mainly a grassed area with some plantings and creepers with buddleia on derelict walls (Plate 5.14). This garden, which has some seating, is that of the Worshipful Company of Plaisterers. At the northern end of Noble Street their rebuilt hall opens

Plate 5.15   St. Olave

onto this open space.

(9) *Noble St. Gardens (St Olave's)* at the junction of London Wall and Noble Street has been developed on the site of a church which was also burned down in the Great Fire (1666) (Plate 5.15). It is a well tended, pleasantly laid out garden using different levels to good effect. It is backed with a good shrub surround, and is separated from London Wall by a conifer tree hedge which provides a reasonable degree of enclosure from the busy main road (Transport and Environment Studies 1985). The garden incorporates several tomb-stones, has grassed areas and a rose bed. Note the excellent young oak tree at the entrance to the green space in Noble Street.

(10) *St Mary Staining* is a green space on the site of St Mary Staining Church which was also destroyed in the Great Fire (1666) and never rebuilt (Plate 5.16).

In Wood Street the trail passes the tower which is all

that remains of St Alban's Church and proceedes along Love Lane to (11) *St Mary Aldermanbury*. The present green space occupies the site of the church and church-yard. It is attractively designed, being composed of a number of different elements. Firstly, at street level, we turn left from Love Lane into a paved area, having as its centrepiece a miniature box hedged knot garden with begonias, surrounded by park seats. Adjacent is an elevated small paved area with a mounted bust of Shakespeare fanning a centrepiece. This intimate area is fronted internally by a yew hedge and surrounded by raised shrub beds and a number of trees, including an Indian bean, which provide a pleasant canopy in summer for the pavements surrounding this space. Finally, there is the largest area, which is found at the lowest part of the garden. This is grassed and occupies the site of the nave of St Mary's and, with the shade of trees, the area provides for pleasant relaxation in hot weather. There is a tablet indicating that the ruins from the church were shipped, stone by stone, to Fulton, Missouri, USA, for re-erection as a memorial to Winston

Plate 5.16   St. Mary Staining

Churchill. Here there is a pathway along the previous north aisle, leading to Aldermanbury, and across the street is the Glass Fountain designed by Allen David and presented to the Corporation in 1969, which forms the frontispiece to a large multilevel hard space precinct behind. At (12) *Aldermanbury Square* a pleasant, yet unpretentious, centrepiece demonstrates how 'greenery' can improve what would otherwise be a dull area, surrounded for the most part by banal buildings, by drawing attention in upon itself. The square traffic island comprises a paved area with a central shrub bed and two trees together with a shrunken fountain and pool. The island is completed by two small semi-circular flower beds with small trees each side of the central bed but separated by a pavement. It was probably within the vicinity of this open space that the English kings had their residence before Edward the Confessor established his palace at Westminster (Plate 5.17).

From here the trail leads to the Barbican which has

formed the City's most ambitious redevelopment programme on a site laid waste during the Second World War. It includes major residential areas, public buildings, the Barbican Arts and Conference Centre, the Barbican Conservatory, and, most importantly for the purposes of this trail, many open and green spaces. The latter are generally private but good panoramic views are afforded from the high level public walkway.

Having crossed London Wall, and before reaching the Podium Public House, turn right along St. Alphage Highwalk and bear left with the walk crossing St. Alphage Garden and then descend the staircase to the lowest level entering (13) *The Salters' Garden*, opened in 1981. This is a distinctive hard surface area with a brick and flagstone floorscape, developed at two levels. There are some well planted shrubberies with trees which flank the less distinguished buildings and provide a visual foil. The Salters' Building itself, which occupies the site of the house of the first Lord Mayor, well offsets a remarkable section of the City Wall which forms the boundary of this garden on the opposite side. The garden landscape is completed by some well stocked planters with palms, and seating is provided. Walk through the gardens passing through a delightful garden annexe, a small paved area with a banked shrub and brilliant flower bed below the road and with creepers overhanging the boundary wall with St. Alphage Place. Ascend the steps to (14) *St. Alphage Place,* which is a small green space with two grassed areas having a magnolia tree on one and an oak on the other. The area is enclosed from the street by a beech hedge and bounded by the City Wall (see plaque no. 12) which separates this area from the Salters' Garden. At the base of the wall is a slightly raised pathway with seating.

Leave by turning right into St Alphage Garden, cross the road and ascend to the high level walkway at the Podium Public House. Follow the yellow line to the Barbican Centre. A few steps further on turn left at Wallside and continue until you face the tower of St Giles Cripplegate. This vantage point presents you with a very good view to (15) *Wallside* open space. A grassed area with a path flanks the building. In places the remains of the City Wall and corner bastion separate the grass from the elongated lake – a pleasant feature with aquatic plants such as reeds and water lilies providing a good and largely undisturbed habitat for a number of birds. On the far side of the lake note St Giles Church, which is set in a rather drab dark brick floorscape especially evident on the north side but pleasantly diffused at this point by a large willow near the church tower and overhanging the lake.

Retrace your steps and, at the junction of Wallside with the Postern, turn left and continue towards the centre viewing the (16) *Andrewes House Gardens* on your right. These small individual plots are pleasantly separated and partially screened from Fore Street by a surround of shrubs and trees.

Now walk onto the bridge across the lake and first take in the view of the (17) *Lakeside Gardens* on your right. The rectangular lake, well stocked with carp, dominates the scene. In the foreground attention is focused on seven small circular islets attached to a central 'channel' and largely covered by creepers on dome-shaped frames (Plate 5.10). In the distance, at the far end of the lake, there is a raised feature with greenery and a water chute which is effective visually as well as helping to exclude less welcome noise. To the far left private wooded gardens join the lakeside. Adjacent to these gardens, and adjoining the main Barbican Centre terrace under the bridge, is a brick floored terrace with seating. Before looking at the contrasting view on the other side of the bridge note the roof garden on the top of the Guildhall School of Music and Drama.

Now cross to the other side of the bridge and view the (18) *Lakeside Terrace* on your left. Again, the area is dominated by the lake with its serried rows of water level fountains (Plate 5.9). Private gardens with a variety of trees and shrubs can be seen in the background beyond the lake. Each side of the lake is dominated by brick paving which has been employed extensively. To the left you can see St Giles set in an 'island' of brick while to the right is the frontage of the Barbican Centre itself. The wide terrace, with numerous tables and chairs in summer, is used by patrons of the restaurant and snack bar. The lakeside fountains, together with planters with shrubs and small trees, go some way to diminish what could be described as the monotonous effect of brick paving (see France 1979) and the inappropriate scatter of tub plantings.

The trail ends at the Barbican Centre with a glimpse of the Conservatory on the left and above on entering.

Notes on the Trails

These two trails show how an element of organisation can be added to walking in the City so that the recreational value of green spaces can be increased. It is stressed that these trails are merely examples and the City has the potential to provide many more.

A major problem with trails of this nature and their accompanying descriptions is the need for constant monitoring and revision due to the rapidly changing townscape. Since these trails were conceived two open spaces on the St Paul's to Barbican trail have disappeared: Brewers Place (between Aldermanbury Square (12) and the Salters' Garden (13)), and Markwell Square (viewed

Plate 5.17   Aldermanbury Square

from the high level walkway between St Alphage Place (14) and Wallside open space (15)). In addition, All Hallows on the Wall ((13) on the Barbican to Liverpool St. trail) has been changed by development, with the loss of the flower beds and seating which greatly alters the character. The trails have been revised to take these changes into acount, but with the present rate of change in the City, no doubt further revisions will be necessary.

Careful consideration must be taken when choosing routes – should the trails be links between major tourist attractions or indeed attractions in their own right? The second trail outlined, although linking attractions, is an example of the latter as it is not purely functional; the visitor must put the trail foremost, as the Barbican can be much more easily reached than by the trail route. Similarly the Barbican to Liverpool Street trail by-passes the stations, making a detour around Cutlers' Court and Devonshire Square. Shorter trails may be devised between attractions which are close together or the trails could have alternative routes so that walkers could choose

the route best suited to their needs.

The St Pauls to Barbican route works particularly well because of its historical content; most spaces have detailed signs and some border the old City Wall such as Wall Green (8), the Salters' Garden (13) and St Alphage Place (14). It could be argued that in addition to having specific green trails, the green spaces heritage of the City should be incorporated into other existing trails such as the London Wall walk or the City Heritage Walk. This would increase awareness of green spaces among people who would not normally be attracted to a full scale Green Trail. The Background Study in Tourism (Corporation of London 1976) mentions the need to signpost attractions, and to 'sell' the City both at home and abroad (8.25). These ideas may be synthesised; the green spaces can be advertised more by the introduction of these trails, and the signposting of attractions can include visits to green spaces as part of the route, for example a sign at St Paul's might read 'Museum of London via Postman's

Park', or at Liverpool Street 'Barbican via Finsbury Circus'.

Discussion and Conclusion

It has already been intimated that the successful management of green and open spaces for people within the City, lies in their integration within the larger perspective of pedestrian movement. Concomitantly, their successful management also lies in their being recognised as a part of the City's tourist potential. The City's gardens and open spaces are as much a part of the City's heritage as are its buildings and institutions. They are intrinsic components of the City's fabric. In some situations green space and open space have been used to advantage in the preservation of archaeological or historic sites incorporating them into a pleasant environmental setting, as we see in the case of the City Wall at St Alphage Place and within the Barbican and elsewhere. It is important therefore that open spaces should be recognised for what they are and that everyone in the City should be encouraged to enjoy them. To challenge people and to stimulate a wider interest in the City's green spaces a ranking system has been devised to encourage people to look a little more closely at green spaces and to assist them to make their own comparative judgements. This is particularly important at the time when a national register and grading system is being devised for parks and gardens (Register of Parks and Gardens of Special Historic Interest).

To encourage further development and use of green spaces four immediate measures can be suggested:

- The establishment of green trails, their discreet sign-posting and the publication and circulation of green trail pamphlets based on the details put forward above for the two pilot trails.

- Publicity: it is necessary to inform visitors about green spaces in the City, and what they are missing by not seeing them through the advertising media.

- It is important to secure the active support and co-operation of the Livery Companies, the Corporation and the various interest groups such as the London Gardens Society, the National Council for the Conservation of Plants and Gardens and the Barbican Horticultural Society, and to provide volunteer green trail guides.

- Green spaces should not be considered apart from, but as an integral part of the City's tourist and environmental brief, to which they make their own unique contribution.

The popularity of trails in towns and cities has increased enormously with the public and, as could be expected, trails cater for an ever widening range of interests. Significantly, parks and garden trails have appeared in a number of cities, for instance there is a 'Central Parks of Southampton' trail. As the City's green spaces are close to one another and as many of these spaces are associated with, or in close proximity to, some of the major City tourist attractions, it would seem sensible to use them more effectively as part of an integrated visitor policy. In so doing the City would be advancing its own objectives as set forth in the City Plan (Corporation of London 1986) 'to encourage better use of existing and potential tourist attractions'. In a small way, by prescribing new possibilities to the more discerning and adventurous visitor, trails, not only green trails, may ease the undoubted congestion around the major city tourist attractions.

Having suggested the development of green trails, and put forward two examples, it is perhaps pertinent to ask three questions:

- Would people use green trails?

- What are the main problems facing green trails in the City?

- What should be done to promote and implement green trails?

It is reasonable to suggest that some 35% of the City's daytime population (including visitors) may have an interest in looking a little more closely at the City's green spaces. The evidence is based on a small questionnaire survey ($n = 75$) carried out in two City streets. It has also been estimated that about one third of the people questioned use open space in the City (see Table 5.4). Further data emphasises the considerable importance of walking in cities. Walk trips account for some 36% of all trips in London (Transport and Environment Studies 1985). It has also been suggested that pleasant pedestrian environments encourage an up to 30% greater walking distance per trip. In London the average walk distance is 1.1 km (Transport and Environment Studies 1985). A pleasant walk might be estimated at 1.4 km, while people walking with a specific objective in mind would no doubt be prepared to walk further. Thus the pilot trail distance of 2-3 km seems not unreasonable especially as there is no imperative to walk the trail from beginning to end.

There are further reasons for supposing that people might be persuaded to follow a green trail. It has been suggested that people appreciate the green City as something which is different, sometimes splendidly different, from the surrounding streets and buildings. The green City is living and constantly changing, indeed the changes through the seasons delight the casual observer as much as the professional photographer. Although summer sees the green spaces at their best, heightening the sense and enjoyment of contrast, the other seasons contribute a charm of their own, making a walk round these open spaces pleasing at any time of the year. In spring there is the sense of anticipation, with buds bursting into blossom, while the many beds of spring bulbs give a strong visual display of colour. Autumn is often described as a season of mellow fruitfulness and in the City's open spaces the visitor can appreciate many rich and warm colours. Winter clearly illuminates the design characteristics of these open spaces as well as providing a patterning of bare branches against the sky or imposed upon surrounding buildings. Also, churchyard evergreens and those more recently planted elsewhere together with shrubs, many with long-lasting berries, can be best appreciated during the City's relatively mild winter.

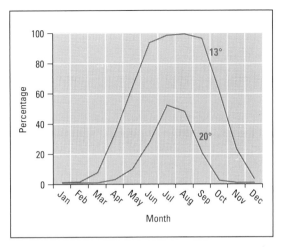

Figure 5.7   The percentage of days in each month that the dry bulb temperature exceeded 13°C and 20°C at 12.00 GMT at the London Weather Centre during 1975-1985.

It has been mentioned that the climate is a major factor governing the recreational use of open spaces. The effect of temperature on walking and recreational activities is subtle compared to heavy and/or continuous rainfall which immediately precludes walking for pleasure. However, evidence suggests a temperature threshold exists at 13°C (55°F), above which a significant amount of pleasure walking begins (Pushkarev and Zupan 1975). A cautious interpretation of Fig. 5.7 suggests that for a considerable part of the year the City enjoys a day temperature in excess of 13°C, especially at the time during the day when most pleasure walking is likely to occur. An examination of the percentage of time temperatures exceed 20°C (Fig. 5.7) shows that, at least during the summer months, it is warm enough to expect a high use of open spaces for sitting or relaxation. In addition, City temperatures are relatively mild over the winter months (during the daytime), a factor which should at least encourage some winter use of City green trails.

People are likely to use green trails in the City if they provide pleasant pedestrian links between important visitor sites such as the main tourist attractions and also links between these sites to and from the main points of departure and arrival of people in the City. (For instance, it has been stated that Liverpool Street Station (BR and LUL) is one of the largest generator of pedestrians in London, (Transport and Environment Studies 1985)) This consideration has been put to a number of people leaving the Barbican Centre, and who appear to support the proposition.

As has already been shown, the two pilot trails have been assessed as generally providing pleasant and attractive pedestrian trails through the City. Others, which would no doubt prove equally attractive, have been suggested. However, it should be noted that such trails are not without their problems, the most important of which can be briefly commented upon under three headings: closure, quality and traffic.

Closure

Although the City Local Plan (Corporation of London 1986) aims to accommodate tourism within the City and to improve the quality of tourist amenities, one of the major problems still confronting the visitor is the virtual shutdown during the evening, particularly unfortunate during the long summer evenings, and at weekends. As has been indicated in the City Local Plan visitors are not likely to spend much time in the City, or walking green trails, when a number of sites are closed in the evenings or at weekends, unless some shops, restaurants, snack bars and public houses are open for business. At weekends green trails can be best utilised as links between tourist attractions since visitors would enjoy largely unimpeded pedestrian movement. This is more difficult to achieve in the more congested areas during the weekdays as working people and visitors will walk at different speeds (see Fruin 1971).

It would therefore seem appropriate for the City to encourage all forms of visitor and tourist activity during 'off peak' times when such activity is least likely to interfere with the City's financial life. Nevertheless, it should be realised that any extension of City life into the summer evenings and at weekends, however desirable, will incur some cost. Locked gardens will need to remain open for longer periods and need additional servicing, and all sites are likely to suffer an increase in the amount of litter to be removed. Also, there may well be an increase in undesirable activities such as vagrancy and vandalism.

Quality

It is generally true to say that the City's green spaces are maintained at a standard which is significantly higher than can be seen elsewhere in the Capital. They would be immediately attractive, on a trail. Nevertheless, the cost of success is eternal vigilance, which means the provision of resources sufficient to meet the increasing cost of maintaining open spaces at the highest standard, at a time when many people's attitudes towards open spaces are increasingly cavalier in an age of fast food and excessive packaging. The litter problem is growing and Cheapside and Moorgate are particularly prone. Unfortunately 'fly tipping' has also been recorded in two green spaces. The person involved was challenged in one instance only to reply that 'the Corporation would clean it away wouldn't they?' During the years since the initial survey there has been an unwelcome increase in litter and, unfortunately, in vagrancy.

The design and landscaping of some open spaces could be improved, although in fairness it must be said that some of the spaces mentioned in the trails have not been specifically conceived of as such. For instance, St Vedast's Place and Brewers' Place are essentially pavement features. However, both offer considerable potential for fuller landscaping. The Goldsmiths' Garden could be improved, access to the sunken section from Gresham Street would be an advantage for a recreational garden, as would be the removal of the over-dominant Indian Bean Tree in this situation. There is also a need for a more decorous treatment of the retaining walls. Again, some changes should be considered for Postman's Park after the restoration of the post office buildings. Now that the coniferous barrier between St Olave's and London Wall is established, their green space could be made more inviting by providing seats. Additional creepers on the derelict wall alongside St Anne and St Agnes and the Noble Street garden would make the view looking north more attractive, adding to the overall sense of harmony in this churchyard. The recent elimination of the last 'wild garden' in the City, adjacent to St Anne and St Agnes on the north side, has been an unfortunate loss. It has been noted that many open spaces on the trails, and elsewhere in the City, have fountains; unhappily, few are in use.

Traffic

The City generates a great deal of vehicular traffic. This is not conducive to pleasant, or even, in some cases, safe walking. However, the green trails have been routed to avoid or lessen traffic conflict wherever possible. Previously, high level walkways were envisaged as a partial solution to this problem. However, such a system, which is suitable to the Barbican and a few adjoining areas, is hardly relevant to the townscape of most of the rest of the City either practically, architecturally or socially.

Basically, the pedestrian wants to move about safely at ground level (Pushkarev and Zupan 1975) and certainly the City suggests it wishes 'to improve facilities and reduce congestion for the pedestrian at street level' (Corporation of London 1986). However, much remains to be done to improve facilities and actually to encourage visitors to walk in the City. Certainly 'ref-

uges' for wide roads are essential as are 'walk' signal phases, as found in French and other continental cities. Again, the pedestrianisation of some streets and alleys would not only aid pedestrian movement but also produce sites for the establishment of further open spaces, hopefully with more flair than several recent drab hard spaces surrounding tall buildings set in from the building line. The importance of the link between easy pedestrian movement and green space is obvious and it is interesting to note that 'pedestrianisation and the provision of trees, shrubs and flowers' are considered to be some of the street improvements necessary if walking in the City is to be taken as seriously as in many comparable European cities (see Transport and Environment Studies 1985, Bernatsky 1975).

Essentially, the City should aim towards the development of recognised pedestrian routes, such as those suggested between visitor attractions, aiming to separate pedestrian and vehicular traffic as much as possible and integrating such routes with present and planned pedestrian walkways, pedestrian areas and the City's open spaces.

St. Dunstan's-in-the-East

CHAPTER 6

City Open Spaces and Nature

Introduction

Studies of urban wildlife have, until fairly recently, always been the poor relation compared with rural wildlife studies. Urban plant communities are often regarded as falling outside the scope of conventional ecology and their study has been largely neglected (Gilbert 1981), while priorities in conservation have been directed almost exclusively towards the animals (and plants) outside urban areas (Benson 1981). The idea that urban habitats are worthwhile both scientifically and socially has gained a great deal of support in recent years and a much greater interest is being taken, by both ecologists and the general public, in city wildlife. In London, public interest has been greatly encouraged by the growth of urban conservation groups.

It should be remembered, however, that city habitats could never be considered as truly 'wild' areas as management levels are so high that natural developments and successions do not occur and are indeed generally not desirable. Habitats of particular importance in the City are the green spaces which include the many churchyards. Other habitats include hard spaces and some aquatic habitats, although these are of secondary importance. City trees are valuable for wildlife, especially when incorporated into green space, although street trees can form biological corridors between green spaces as well as being a habitat in their own right.

This chapter will consider the composition and vegetational diversity of green space habitats, examine the biological role of trees in the City, and survey the bird life of the City. Some concluding remarks will consider the advantages and disadvantages of encouraging wildlife in the City.

Habitats in the City

The urban environment provides a number of interlinked habitats in an uneven distribution. In the City of London such habitats include buildings, roads, small parks and squares, street gardens, churchyards, artificial lakes and the River Thames. These habitats may be classified as follows:

- Green spaces and street gardens, comprising flower beds, grass, trees and shrubs.

- Hard spaces, comprising brick, concrete and stone, although planters and tubs are usually present.

- Aquatic habitats, comprising small lakes, fountains and the river.

Plate 6.1 Churchyard of St. Botolph's, Bishopsgate

Green Space

The most common green space habitat in the City is 'amenity grassland', the vegetation being predominantly grasses (*Graminae*) with trees and shrubs (Plate 6.1). These grass areas have an open nature and are artificially created and maintained with fertilizers, as in Finsbury Circus, Bishopsgate Churchyard and the green spaces around St Paul's. The grassed areas may be subjected to trampling, especially if specific routes are used. Not only does trampling cause physical damage to plants, it also brings about soil compaction, leading to a reduction in soil aeration, and can prevent the movement of water through the soil, thus affecting vegetation. Soil compaction and loss of vegetation is evident in Trinity Square (although strictly outside the City) and around the single tree at the junction of Houndsditch and Outwich Street, while some grassed areas close to roads may be affected by pollution.

Other green space habitats are ornamental flowerbeds, although these are less valuable for wildlife. They often contain non-native species and cultivars, little ground is left bare, and weed species are not tolerated, so providing fewer opportunities for wildlife to exploit. These planted ornamental areas have largely been ignored by plant ecologists as the usual physical parameters of soil and climate do not apply, their existence being governed by function, prestige, fashion and cost of maintenance (Gilbert 1981).

As most of the open spaces in the City are intensively managed (Fiebig 1982), most dead material is removed from the site, so a valuable microhabitat of rotting vegetation or compost is lost.

Hard Space

Most of the fabric of the City consists of hard substrate habitats (including buildings) (Plate 6.2). Surfaces such as concrete and brick affect the ability of plants to germinate and put down roots, restrict sites for invertebrates, and limit opportunities for wildlife through their lack of moisture. The major hard space habitats in the City are:

- **Paved Surfaces**: these offer little opportunity

for the establishment of plant life unless the slabs are weathered, cracked or uneven. The spaces between paving stones offer opportunities for hardy grasses and mosses, but high water loss and excessive trampling prevent most plants from establishing themselves.

- **Asphalt Surfaces**: these are less common in the City and include the courts in Bishopsgate Churchyard. Although most plants take root in surface cracks on the asphalt, some manage to push up from below. Initial colonisers include the silver thread moss (*Bryum argentum*) which encourages other plants by a substrate produced on decomposition.

The walls of the City provide an extensive third hard space habitat, although their value differs with age, situation, aspect and composition. These factors determine the likely moisture content of the wall – a major factor in determining its suitability for wildlife, although the funnelling of wind around buildings can cause other problems for colonisers.

Plate 6.2   Aldermanbury, Guildhall

Plate 6.3   Lakeside Terrace, Barbican

Aquatic Habitats

Although much water has been conduited, the City of London provides some aquatic habitats including the Thames and the Barbican lakes (Plate 6.3). If water is present, aquatic wildlife can flourish, although artificially created bodies of water often tend to be straight-edged with steep sides, providing limited opportunities for exploitation by plants and animals. Until recently the Thames has been restricted by development; the British Trust for Conservation Volunteers are currently working on a project to establish emergent plants along the embankments.

Other habitats occasionally found in the City are areas of waste or vacant land. These sites are usually only temporary, but they can include strips of land between buildings which are unsuitable for development, and untended patches in parks and gardens. The Second World War brought about a large increase in the amount of vacant land in the City but nearly all of this has been redeveloped.

Plots of vacant land will support unsown, unmanaged, spontaneous vegetation, mostly at a fairly early successional stage. These sites tend to suffer a high degree of disturbance and are most suitable for plants with either a ruderal or competitive strategy. Unkempt areas such as wastelands are generally regarded as undesirable. A problem is that although they may look pleasing during the flowering period, once die-back occurs, the City inhabitant, accustomed to seeing the selected, generally evergreen vegetation of the urban garden, will often regard the wasteland site as 'untidy', particularly if litter is allowed to accumulate (Gilbert 1981).

An increasing number of plant habitats are now provided within building developments in the City. In such a controlled environment a further variety of plants may well be used (Collins 1984).

The Vegetation of the City

Plant communities in the City fall into two categories: unsown vegetation, and planted ornamental vegetation, the majority falling into the latter category. The unsown vegetation category includes spontaneous, unmanaged vegetation which is usually at a fairly early stage of succession. Such vegetation, often found on areas of wasteland and plots awaiting development, can be invaluable to wildlife. Many of the plant species which colonise sites in the City, such as sorrel (*Rumex acetosella*) and ribwort plantain (*Plantago lanceolata*), have been part of the British flora for many centuries (Collins 1984). Such species can often support a greater and more diverse fauna than the non-native cultivars found in planted ornamental gardens.

Some non-native species have, however, rapidly become integrated into the food webs and a particular urban example is the butterfly bush (*Buddleia davidii*), introduced into Britain around 1896 as an ornamental bush and now conspicuous on development sites, wasteland and along railways.

Derelict wasteland and the associated plant communities are now being recognised as being of considerable local and regional significance as refuges for uncommon and even rare plants such as London rocket (*Sisymbrium irio*) (Johnson 1978, Bradshaw 1971). They are also very vulnerable, especially in the City of London where pressures for development are intense, and land is rarely allowed to lie derelict for long enough to become colonised.

Planted ornamental areas in the City such as parks, gardens, street planters and window boxes can also be useful for wildlife. They are, however, often planted with exotic species and other plants less useful to British wildlife. Possible ways of increasing their usefulness will be discussed later in the chapter.

In some areas, such as Finsbury Circus and Bishopsgate Churchyard, the traditional public park grassland of tough, short rye grass (*Lolium* spp.) is appropriate because the areas are subject to the pressures of people. However, there are a few areas in the City where herb-rich meadows could be established. These areas include the small pockets of grass which are established purely for visual purposes and are not subject to trampling. Establishing a species-rich sward could be more visually stimulating, as well as reducing costs for the area through its less intensive management needs. However, a species-rich sward with its informal appearance is not desirable in most City open spaces as often the formality of a short cropped lawn is required as an extension of an architectural feature.

If planted with the right flowers a flower border or window box in a sheltered, sunny position will provide pollen and nectar for a great variety of insects throughout the spring, summer and early autumn (Emery 1986). A simple alteration in the plant species used in herbaceous borders, from the unexploitable cultivars and unproductive hybrids to the native and non-native species known to be beneficial to wildlife, will not cause these formal plantings to be any less attractive to humans and may in some cases bring about great improvements. Although plants such as nettles (*Urtica* spp.), thistles (*Cirsiums* spp.), and docks (*Rumex* spp.), which are invaluable food plants for insects, may be considered undesirable by people, there are many flowring plants which can fulfil both these functions. These include lupins (*Lupinus polyphyllus*), snapdragons (*Antirrhinum majus*), aubretia (*Aubretia deltoidea*) and primrose (*Primula vulgaris*).

Vegetational Diversity in City Green Spaces

In an attempt to assess the variety of habitats and 'richness' of the green spaces of the City a vegetation diversity index was used. This quantified the various habitats present in the City of London so that a comparison of sites, both within and outside the core area of the City, could be made. This assessment used criteria set out in detail below. The City is a managed plant environment and although the ideas of richness and diversity (Spellerberg 1981) are designed for 'natural' communities, some aspects can be recorded and used for this study. The information was used to ascertain whether a relationship existed between the size of a green space and its vegetational diversity. Special emphasis was given to the presence of trees, while the presence of shrubs and herbs was also taken

Plate 6.4   Middle Temple Garden

into account (Plate 6.4).

Compilation of the index involved alloting points for each of the variables involved; these were:

- **Presence of herb, shrub and tree layers:** 1 point for each present, giving a maximum score of 3 points.

- **Number of trees present:** for under 5 trees 1 point is scored, for 5-15 trees 2 points, for more than 15 trees, 3 points.

- **Number of tree species present:** one point for each species.

- **Tree value**, based on data given by Southwood (1961), considers the value of trees for associated British insect species. Each tree was placed in one of the five groups shown in Table 6.1 and the scores added to give a tree

value for each area as a whole.

- **Tree age:** saplings and young trees were given one point each and mature trees two points.

The scores for each of the five variables were added together to give the vegetation diversity index.

Previously a rurality index (Table 3.2) has been calculated for twenty of the thirty-one major green spaces in the City. This information was used to ascertain whether there was any correlation between the apparent rurality of an open space and its vegetation diversity.

Figure 6.1 shows the calculated vegetation diversity index numbers for each of the thirty-one sites surveyed plotted against the size of each of the sites. The degree of association and regression line have been calculated and there is a positive, though fairly weak, correlation between the size of an open space and its diversity of vegetation.

Table 6.1	Grouping of trees according to their value with respect to associated insect species. The scores were used in the calculation of a vegetation diversity index (see text).

Group A (4 points)	Group B (3 points)	
Oak, pedunculate & sessile		
Blackthorn		
Willow sp.	Hawthorn	
Birch sp.	Poplar sp.	
Crab apple		
Alder	Pine, Scots	

Group C (2 Points)	Group D (1 point)	Group E (0 point)
Elm	Lime	Other species
Hazel	Hornbeam	
Beech	Rowan	
Ash	Maple	
Spruce	Juniper	
Larch		
Fir		
Sycamore		
Holly		
Chestnut		
Yew		
Walnut		
Holm oak		
Plane		

The correlation is rather stronger between area size and vegetation diversity for the twenty sites outside the core area of the City of London. This includes such sites as St Paul's Churchyard and Postman's Park.

For the sites within the core area of the City, including such open green spaces as St Anne and St Agnes Churchyard and St Michael's, Cornhill, a weak positive correlation is evident but the data is limited to only eleven open green spaces.

The vegetation diversity index number was also plotted against the calculated rurality index but there appeared to be no correlation between the two.

The vegetation diversity indices calculated range from 1 at Noble Street, Fetter Lane and Austin Friars to 79 in St Paul's Churchyard and 80 in the Cannon Street/ New Change Garden (area 11, site 4). The mean

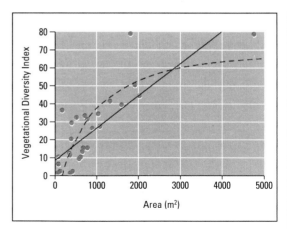

Figure 6.1   Vegetation diversity indices (derived as explained in text) for 31 green spaces in the City of London plotted against the area of those spaces.

indices and sizes of core, non-core and all sites combined are shown in Table 6.2.

Table 6.2	Mean areas and vegetation diversity indices for Green Spaces in the City of London

	Mean Vegetation Diversity Index	Mean Size (m²)
All sites	24.3	851
Core sites	19.4	673
Non-core sites	27.0	949

Figure 6.2 shows the distribution of the vegetation diversity indices. It can be seen that the smaller indices are most common, with over 51% of green spaces in the City having a vegetation diversity index of less than 20.

Although there does seem to be some positive correlation between area and diversity of vegetation, it cannot be said that the vegetational diversity is a result of the size of the area. It is most likely that the vegetation diversity is a result of the interaction of such factors as area, management regimes, site and situation and intensity of public use. Such a conclusion is backed up by Fiebig's (1982) summary, especially the influence of

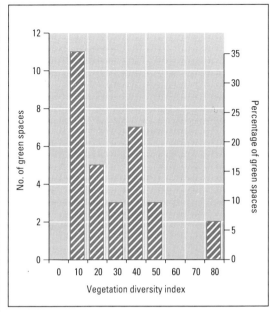

Figure 6.2 Frequency of occurrence of vegetation diversity indices in a sample of 31 green spaces in the City of London.

Plate 6.5 Information Centre Garden

management.

Although most City green spaces have a low vegetational diversity, this does not necessarily mean that their vegetational aesthetics are low. The 'rurality' of a green space is influenced to a certain extent by diversity, but other factors must also be taken into consideration such as noise, screening, etc (Plate 6.5). An example of high vegetational diversity is Seething Lane Gardens, however, although well stocked with a wide variety of species, the noise from the road and passing aircraft detract from the rural atmosphere. Trees function as good insulators of noise and can increase the vegetational aesthetics and give a 'rural feel' to areas. In order to assess the City tree population the following survey was undertaken.

A Survey of City Trees

Open Space in the City is much improved by the presence of trees, whether in green space, hard space or within planters. Trees contribute to both physical quality (by filtering the air, stabilising temperatures and reducing the wind funnel effects of buildings), and to the perceived quality of the urban environment (bringing pleasure, reducing environmental stress). Trees are the most visible aspect of nature in the urban landscape, whether in open space or in the City streets. Although the importance of trees in improving open space is widely recognised, street trees are of great value, adding an element of rurality to the wider built environment. A truly 'green city' needs more than isolated green spaces or street planters; street trees play an important part in visually linking the open spaces of the City, as well as providing communication corridors for wildlife. However, street trees are not without problems – in summer they can cause soil shrinkage; as they mature, roots can interfere with below-ground services; and their planting and management costs can be high. Indeed they are sometimes considered as having little importance, and that the money spent on them would be better redirected to more immediate concerns.

This study examines the distribution and types of tree present in the City, in order to quantify the present population and to help in planning the future of the City's trees.

Method

Although trees are a major natural feature of the City of London, information on tree numbers, species and ages is very limited and detailed management records are not kept. Trees are planted by both public and private bodies, making it difficult to keep up-to-date tree records. To ascertain knowledge of the characteristics of the tree population of the City and thereby assess present day and future problems a comprehensive survey of the City's trees was needed.

Data were obtained from the Tree Record File, Department of Parks and Gardens, Corporation of London, updated to 1976. This information was further updated using data obtained from surveys carried out by the City of London Polytechnic in 1982-4 and 1984-6.

In order to give a smaller scale picture and to ease the problems of data collection and co-ordination the City was divided into twenty areas of varying sizes (see p.17). Some areas were so small that in certain cases statistics were combined to give larger samples and more meaningful results, so that 17 areas are recognised overall.

A measure of the approximate age of each tree was found using the girth measurement at shoulder height. The trees were placed into four age categories: saplings, up to 0.15 metres (also staked trees); young, 0.16 - 0.34 metres; mature, 0.35 - 1.80 metres; and over-mature, over 1.81 metres (also trees with dead branches and or in need of support). This was a flexible system taking into account the fact that some trees, such as *Betula* species, mature more quickly than others, such as *Quercus* and *Platanus* sp.

The statistics were used to ascertain the numbers and species of trees present, age structures, densities, and information on the sapling and over-mature tree populations, to enable an assessment to be made of the City's tree population. The City is home to 1885 street trees, comparing favourably to totals for similar sized

areas in the West End (1,162) and neighbouring Tower Hamlets (1,916). The most commonly occurring tree in the City of London is the plane tree, which represents 22.6 per cent of the total trees in the City, but only 13.3 per cent of the total trees in the West End and 12.6 per cent of the trees in Tower Hamlets. The plane is the principal species in most European towns – it accounts for 40 per cent of trees in Paris (Duvigneaud 1975).

Species

Seventy species, both native and exotic, were identified in the sample of 1885 City trees. Of these the ten most common species were: *Platanus acerifolia* (London plane), *Tilia* sp. (mostly *Tilia x europaea* and *T. platyphyllos*), *Prunus* sp. (cherry trees), *Acer* sp. (including Norway maple and sycamores), *Betula* sp. (mostly silver birch), *Fraxinus excelsior* (common ash), *Sorbus* sp. (mainly *Sorbus aria*, whitebeam), *Abies sp.* (Firs), *Fagus sylvatica* (beech), and *Salix alba* (white willow). These ten species accounted for over 69 per cent of the total tree population and their numbers are shown in Fig. 6.3.

Of the 70 tree species found in the City of London only 15 were native, 36% of the total tree population. Of the 32 sapling species 10 were native and the 82 saplings accounted for almost 45% of the sapling population. Native species are important in that they tend to support greater numbers of species of birds and insects than exotic species.

Age

Of the 1885 trees present 186 (9.8%) were saplings, 932 (49.0%) were young, 624 (33.1%) were mature and 143 (7.6%) were over-mature (Fig. 6.4). This seems to give a fairly well balanced age structure with some 59% of the trees not yet mature.

Age structures for each of the ten most common species were also calculated. *Platanus acerifolia* (Fig. 6.5) was found to have only 1.6% of its population in the sapling group and 26.2% of its trees over-mature, with some of these trees over 80 years old. This could pose future problems not only for the survival of the London

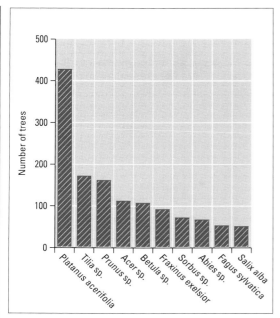

Figure 6.3   Actual numbers of the most common species of tree found in the City of London.

plane in the City but also for the City's tree population as a whole, as these over-mature planes make up over 6% of the total tree population. There also appear to be relatively few *Tilia* saplings, but over 50% of the lime trees are in the young category and under 4% in the

over-mature category. No over mature specimens of *Betula* sp., *Fraxinus excelsior, Abies* sp., *Fagus sylvatica* or *Salix alba* occur; this is probably because they are relatively fast growing, shortlived trees which do not grow large enough in girth size to be placed in the over- mature category and also do not survive to great enough ages to give the appearance of over-maturity, that is, tend not to become stag-headed or need support. *Betula* sp., *Sorbus* sp. and *Abies* sp. have very young populations with relatively large percentages of saplings. This can be considered more fully in Fig. 6.6. The total sapling population contains 32 species and of which 11 comprise some 77.4% of the total sapling population. The most commonly planted saplings are *Betula* sp., *Sorbus* sp., *Prunus* sp. and *Abies* sp. and if this trend continues the City's tree population will in the future cease to be dominated by planes and limes.

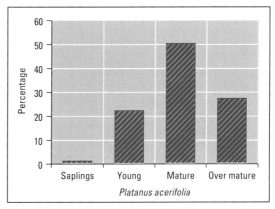

Figure 6.5   The age structure of the population of the most commonly occuring species of tree, *Platanus acerifolia*, in the City of London (*n* = 426).

Density and Distribution of Trees

Information on the numbers of trees present was also used to calculate the densities of trees in each of the seventeen areas of the City recognised in this survey. The size of these areas ranged from 35,956 m² to areas over six times this size at 217,961 m². Figure 6.7 shows the numbers of trees per hectare for each of the areas. (Areas 2 and 5, 7 and 8 and 14 and 20 have been added together to give reasonable-sized working areas and samples.) Area 15, located in the south-west of the City, was found to have the highest tree density, it being a fairly small area of some 72,357 m² containing 151 trees. High numbers of trees were found in

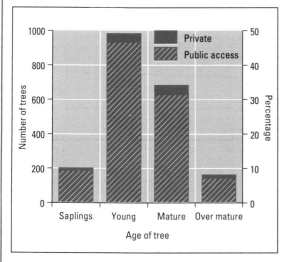

Figure 6.4   The numbers and relative abundance of trees within four age classes (*n*=1885).

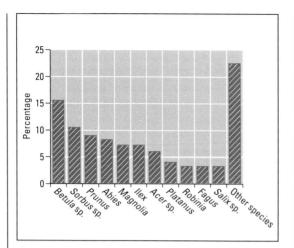

Figure 6.6 The relative abundance of the most common tree species in the total sapling population of 186 in the City of London.

this area due to the presence of the Inner Temple and Middle Temple gardens and the trees along part of the Victoria Embankment. Area 11, located in the centre of the City, also had a high tree density, being one of the largest areas (21,7961 m²), containing 388 trees. The high tree densities are due to the several parks and open spaces and many street trees in this area, including Postman's Park, the Guildhall, the Festival Garden and St Paul's Churchyard. In the southeast of the City, area 19 was also found to have a high tree density due to the high numbers of trees around the Custom House, Seething Lane garden and Fenchurch Street.

The lowest tree density was found in the northeast of the City in area 7/8, comprising 133,767 m² but containing only 38 trees. The lack of trees was due to

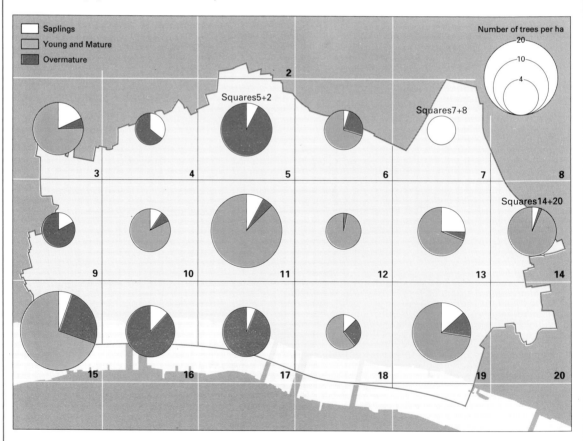

Figure 6.7 The density of trees in different areas of the City of London, and the proportions of the tree population in three age categories.

approximately half of the area being taken up by Liverpool Street Station and the former Broad Street Station. The remainder of the area is also built up and no gardens are present. Area 4, in the northwest of the City, an area of 128,155 m^2, contained only 44 trees; the low tree density is due to the expanse of Smithfield markets and a lack of open green or hard spaces. Most of the trees here were located around St Bartholomew's and West Smithfield. Only 85 trees were found in the 217,961 m^2 of area 12, in the centre of the City. In this area, around Bank and Moorgate South, there is a very high density of buildings and very few open spaces. Most of the trees were situated around Gt Winchester Street, St Michael's, Cornhill, and St Olave's, Ironmonger Lane.

From Fig. 6.7 it can also be seen that no saplings were recorded in areas 4 and 7/8 and there was also a low density of saplings in area 12. The highest sapling densities were to be found in areas 3, 11 (St Paul's), 13, 15, 16 and 19. Area 3 shows a high density because it is a very small area, there being only six saplings actually present. The high number of saplings per hectare in area 13 is mainly due to the tree plantings in the new Cutlers' Court complex.

The number of over-mature trees per hectare for each area is also shown in Fig. 6.7. It can be seen that in areas 7/8, 9, 16 and 17 no over-mature trees were recorded. This is to be expected in areas 7/8 and 9 as the overall tree densities are low in these areas. In areas 16 and 17 the overall tree densities are fairly high and the sapling densities are also high, pointing to a young tree population in these areas.

The highest numbers of over-mature trees per hectare are found in areas 15 (Inner and Middle Temple gardens), 19 (Eastcheap area), 4 (Smithfields) and 6 (Finsbury Circus and Moorgate). In areas 4 and 6 the overall tree densities are low: area 4 has no saplings and area 6 has a low density of saplings, showing that the tree populations in these areas are unbalanced and that new planting is needed to ensure that trees remain in these areas. Despite its very high numbers of over-mature trees per hectare area 15 also has a high sapling density, giving a more stable population overall, and this is also true for area 19.

Discussion

There are just under two thousand trees in the City of London, located in parks, gardens, churchyards and on streets. A wide variety of species are present and the diversity is greatest among the more recently planted trees (Plates 6.6 – 6.11). In natural communities species diversity is generally considered to be desirable, but according to Richards (1983) in the artificial urban environment there is a good case for restricting the numbers of species present to those species which have proved their ability to survive the rigours of urban life. Most essential for a stable population is a good age diversity so that successful replacements are always available. As Richards (1983) states: 'In street tree populations, stability depends primarily on the longevity of individual trees and sufficient numbers of successful planted replacements.'

For the City of London as a whole the age diversity of the tree population is good, with almost 60 per cent of the population not yet mature. However, when considered on a smaller scale it can be seen that in certain areas of the City the age structure of the tree population is unbalanced. For instance in the Smithfields and Finsbury Circus/Moorgate areas there are more over-mature trees than there are saplings and this could soon lead to a dramatic fall in the tree populations in these areas. The delightful Finsbury Circus is very vulnerable in that much of its present state of isolation is brought about by the outer circle of London plane trees, all of which are over-mature.

To the south of the City sapling densities are relatively high, indicating fairly stable populations. New plantings, however, are welcomed where suitable sites are available.

The number of trees per hectare varies greatly across the City, from the lowest densities in the Liverpool Street, Smithfields and Bank areas, to the highest densities in the Middle and Inner Temple, and St Paul's areas.

Age diversity also differs from species to species. In recent years the most commonly found tree in the City, the London plane (*Platanus acerifolia*), has not been

A variety of city trees   **Plate 6.6**   London Wall

Plate 6.7   Barbican

Plate 6.8   Paternoster Square

Plate 6.9   Austral House Place

Plate 6.10   Aldermanbury Square

Plate 6.11   Cutlers Court

favoured and this is shown by the fact that less than 2% of plane trees are saplings and almost 27% are over-mature. These over-mature planes account for over 6% of the total tree population of the City and their loss could have a dramatic impact on the appearance of the City. Lime trees (*Tilia* sp.) appear to have a more stable population than the plane, but it may not be long before they too become unstable, as few sapling limes are being planted and there is a high percentage of mature to over-mature trees in the lime population.

The most commonly planted saplings are birch, whitebeam, cherry and fir species (Fig. 6.6); these make up almost 45 per cent of the sapling population. Of these, birch species are favoured because of their graceful appearance and canopy which does not give excessive shade; *Sorbus* sp. are small to medium sized trees bearing attractive foliage and fruit; cherry species are favoured for their colourful blossoms and generally small to medium size; while fir species are popular because their evergreen foliage provides colour and cover all year round.

Robinia pseudoacacia was previously fairly popular but plantings have declined as there is a tendency for branches to break. *Salix* species are also not popular as they tend to be very water demanding and can cause clay shrinkage and pipe blockage. The great variety of sapling species includes many exotics paid for or donated by foreign visitors or governments who often choose a tree species representative of their country.

For wildlife in the City it is generally more beneficial to plant native tree species as these provide the food and cover to support more species of birds, animals and insects than do exotics. Over recent years this has become more understood and there may have been a move towards planting more native species, in that only 36% of the total tree population are native whereas 45% of the sapling population are native trees. However, it must be remembered that not all British trees are suitable for urban environments and some non-native trees such as the Norway maple (*Acer platanoides*) and the sycamore (*Acer pseudoplatanus*) are well adapted for a city existence.

A major problem for trees in the City is lack of water,

and there is often great concern over the amount of damage trees cause to the urban fabric both physically and through causing clay shrinkage. It is important, therefore, to know which trees are particularly water demanding to avoid planting them close to buildings or on clay soils liable to shrink. The relative abundance of the most water demanding species in the City tree population is shown in Fig. 6.8. There were 1,109 of these trees, accounting for 58.8% of the trees in the City. However, water demanding trees accounted for only 38% of the sapling population.

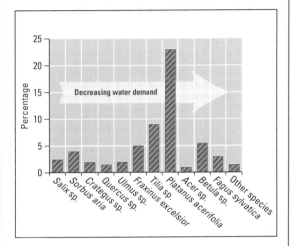

Figure 6.8   The relative abundance of the eleven most water demanding species of trees in the City of London population of 1885 trees of 72 species.

Fewer water demanding species have been planted in the City, especially since the drought of 1976. During the summer, trees in the City are also sprayed with S600, an anti-transpirant, to help prevent excess water loss through transpiration. Structural problems caused by trees have in some cases been overplayed, and most damage caused by soil shrinkage by tree roots is of a comparatively minor nature, most damage being only cosmetic and not requiring extensive repairs (Tomlinson *et al* 1978). Drought accounted for the loss of twelve sapling oaks in 1976 but this was probably a rare occurrence and due to the fact that the young trees had been planted late and had not yet fully established their root systems. In future more careful planting in more suitable sites could prevent such losses.

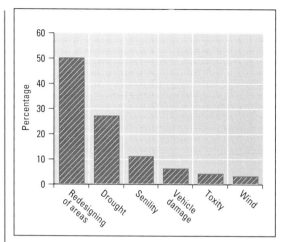

Figure 6.9   The percentages of trees lost within a five year period in the City of London from six major causes.

Trees of all sizes are lost from the population for a variety of reasons including vehicle damage, drought, and the redesigning and redevelopment of areas. Over a five year period 74 trees were removed, an average of almost 15 per annum. Figure 6.9 shows the percentages of trees lost in the six categories – redesigning of areas, drought, senility, vehicle damage, toxity and wind – over the five year period. The biggest losses (67.6%) were due to the redesigning of areas, in which fifty young *Robinia pseudoacacia* were lost.

Apart from loss through re-development of areas, relatively few trees are lost each year; however, new plantings must continue to ensure that the City's tree population remains stable. Where trees do cause problems such as excessive shading or obstruction, careful pruning or tree surgery can be used. Techniques such as crown lifting, the careful removal of lower branches, can alleviate problems of pedestrian access and obstructed vehicular sight lines. Where a tree has become too big for a site skilful crown reduction can be used to reduce the size of the tree. Pruning was formerly a major part of urban tree maintenance; however, since the 1970s amenity societies have been calling for trees to be left in more natural shapes.

Leaking chemicals and air pollution affect trees, and such problems as these, along with vandalism and impact injuries, lead to trees which are less able to withstand diseases.

Common tree diseases include Anthracnose, a fungal disease prevalent in London planes and *Salix* species. Fire blight affects *Crataegus* sp. causing the wilting of young shoots and foliage, turning affected areas black or brown. Beech bark disease leads to tree death, control being very difficult, whereas control of such problems such as wilts and cankers generally involves removal and sanitary disposal of affected branches. A more satisfactory option is problem prevention – by stimulating optimum growing conditions, providing trees with adequate space, planting in areas with favourable soil texture, moisture and orientation, improving drainage, adding fertilisers and selecting trees resistant to disease, tree weakness can be prevented, leading to less disease (Pitt, Soergill and Zube 1979).

Vandalism is a problem most prevalent in the establishment years of a tree. If possible it is best to plant trees with a clear stem of over 2 metres and an overall height of 4 to 5 metres so that branches are out of reach. Involvement of the City business community in planting and caring for their trees could also combat vandalism.

Several factors must be taken into account when deciding which tree species to plant. Consideration must be made as to the size a tree is likely to grow to and whether these proportions will be suitable for the site concerned. The siting of a tree must cause no inconvenience to traffic and must not obstruct vehicle or pedestrian sight lines (Plate 6.12). Allowance must be made for the root run of the tree, avoiding planting deep or wide rooting species in limited spaces. Trees must be available from good, disease-free stock. The species chosen should harmonise with the surrounding buildings, to emphasise or play down textures and architectural shapes. The species chosen should also be suitable for urban environments and should be easy to manage to avoid expensive maintenance costs. Species such as *Robinia pseudoacacia* and *Ailanthus altissima*, which were formerly popular city trees are being planted much less widely now due to management problems caused by broken and decayed branches.

In recent years the practice of planting trees in planters

Plate 6.12

Aldermanbury,
Love Lane

and 'street gardens' has become more common. For planters a minimum depth of half a metre is necessary but generally approximately 2 metres is allowed. The planters are often underlaid with concrete, so care must be taken in choosing trees of a suitable size. However, there are many examples of 'mismatch' planting and/ or poor maintenance.

For effective management to take place it is necessary to maintain up-to-date tree management records. However, tree management is generally not of a high priority and few cities have such a detailed, computerised recording system as that established in Washington, DC, by their Dept. of Highways and Traffic (Pitt,

Soergill and Zube 1979). The planting and care of trees is often seen as uneconomic, as the initial outlay is great, with no monetary return. Management costs are high as the density of the city's buildings and pedestrian movement means that regular maintenance is necessary to safeguard against possible adverse effects on the buildings or the public. Maintenance costs for the city may also be increased due to the added stress to trees in the built environment, through the effects of pollution, wind funnelling, vehicular damage and, to a lesser extent, vandalism. However, this cost can be justified by the way in which trees (and green spaces) do improve both the actual and perceived quality of the urban environment.

Wildlife in the City

The City does not offer many places for wild animals to live, or very much for them to eat except man's waste. Only the most adaptable species can modify their behaviour and eating habits sufficiently to live among offices and busy streets. The ubiquitous town pigeons and house sparrows live the whole of their lives in the City, eating, breeding and sleeping there. Other birds such as starlings still depend on the open country-side for their food but come into the City in huge flocks for warmth and freedom from predators at night. Not all predators are absent, however; both tawny owls and kestrels are known to nest and feed in central London.

In theory, all green plants in the City provide a potential source of food and shelter for small birds and animals. However, two features may reduce their use-fulness in this respect: firstly, non-native plant species are less likely to harbour native insects and so provide less food for birds such as tits and robins *; secondly, the patches of vegetation may be too small and isolated to provide either enough food or sufficient cover. Species such as blackbirds, which feed mostly on soil animals, will only be found where there is open soil with worm casts, and bushes and shrubs (for shelter and nest sites). Larger patches of vegetation together with native species of trees and shrubs are thus pre-ferred by wildlife. Moreover, diversity of structure, that is, between grass, shrubs and trees, which leads to a greater diversity of species, is more likely to encourage a variety of birds than a restricted vegetational environment.

Trees which are good for wildlife and also suited to urban conditions include ash (*Fraxinus excelsior*), birches (*Betula* spp.) (although the Silver birch does not seem to thrive in London), hornbeam (*Carpinus betulus*), limes (*Tilia* spp.) and *Sorbus* spp. Shrub species which fulfil these conditions include elder (*Sambucus nigra*), hawthorn (*Crataegus* spp.), holly (*Ilex aquifolium*) and dogrose (*Rosa canina*). Holly and hawthorn make excellent nest sites as the thorns discourage predators

and inquisitive humans. Evergreens are exceptionally useful as roosting sites during the winter, so there is a place for exotic conifers and other evergreen shrubs along with yew (*Taxus baccata*) and holly.

Where hedging is required it is a relatively simple matter to replace non-native species of privets and conifers with native species such as hawthorn, hazel (*Corylus avellana*), rowan (*Sorbus aucuparia*) and na-tive privet (*Ligustrum vulgare*).

Although there are plants in the City that can support much wildlife, the most common animals found are those that have adapted best to the man-made environ-ment, that is, are able to exploit man-made habitats and man's waste. In addition, species must be highly mobile to reach inner City areas, and be highly mobile within these areas in order to escape from danger and to search for food. It is not surprising, therefore, that the most common and best adapted species are birds.

The feral pigeon (*Columba livia*) is probably more dependent on man than any other bird. Virtually all of their food is provided intentionally or unintentionally by man, and man-made structures are used as roosting and nesting sites (Owen 1978).

Animals with specific food requirements, a need for space or lack of disturbance cannot easily adapt to a city existence, but when the urban landscape can be ex-ploited, numbers of a certain species may become greater in urban areas than in the countryside. For example, blackbirds (*Turdus merula*) have consistently higher population densities in urban and suburban areas than in rural areas (Batten 1973). The first recorded case of blackbirds breeding in the City of London was in 1949 on a bombsite near St. Paul's Cathedral (Owen 1978). Blackbirds born and bred in towns tend to remain there throughout their lives. The move from rural to urban areas has resulted in a larger population of blackbirds and also a smaller migratory population. House sparrows (*Passer domesticus*), swifts (*Apus apus*) and housemartins (*Delichon urbica*) are also now more closely associated with towns than with other habitats.

* Figures indicate that the top five trees acting as hosts for more than 100 species of insects all occur in the City (Southwood 1961). They are the oak, willow, birch, hawthorn and poplar. However, two of the most common trees in the City (the plane and true acacia) are hosts for only one insect species between them. Generally, introduced tree species are host to fewer insects than indigenous ones (Emery 1986).

Amongst the bird species known to breed in the City of London are wrens (*Troglodytes troglodytes*), mistle thrush (*Turdus viscivorus*), kestrel (*Falco tinnunculus*), wood pigeon (*Columba palumbus*), greenfinch (*Cardvelis chloris*) and goldfinch (*Cardvelis cardvelis*) (Montier 1977). Although tawny owls (*Strix aluco*) have been known to breed in the St. Paul's area a recent survey called Owl Prowl, organised by the London Wildlife Trust, failed to produce any sightings of any owl species in the city, although tawny owls were seen in Berkely Square, Bloomsbury and Knightsbridge (Isles 1987).

A move from countryside to urban areas constitutes a major environmental change which may lead to evolutionary adaption. As evolution is generally a very slow process, little evidence yet exists, but among species which have adapted to town life by responding quickly to environmental changes are the peppered moth (*Biston betularia*) and scalloped moth (*Odontopera bidentata*), both of which are polymorphic species whose populations become dominated by forms whose colouring blended in with the lichen-less trees of polluted city areas (Owen 1978).

Mammals in the City of London tend to be scarce mainly due to disturbance and lack of breeding sites. Grey squirrels (*Sciurus carolinensis*), an introduction from North America, are well established in urban areas, including the City, particularly in parks where natural food supplies are supplemented by food offered by people (Plate 6.14). Smaller mammals including the house mouse (*Mus musculus*) and the common rat (*Rattus norvegicus*) are also commonly found in cities. Bats successfully use buildings for breeding and hibernation, and although relatively little was known about bat populations, interest in them has grown rapidly. Although no sightings were recorded for the City in the London Bat Project (launched in 1984 by the Fauna and Flora Preservation Society), it is possible that bats do use the City for roosting and hunting (Mickleburgh 1985).

Decaying organic material remaining in open spaces provides a home for hibernating invertebrates; dead wood also encourages fungi, moulds and other decomposers. However these habitats are very rare in the City due to the intensive management of green spaces, as grass cuttings and other waste material are quickly removed from the site.

Birds in the Open Spaces of the City

Of the animal species found in the City, birds are the most numerous, the most interesting to the public and, just as important, the species with which people most readily identify, feeding birds being the only direct contact with nature for many urban dwellers and office workers (Plate 6.13). A bird survey was carried out to add to the very limited amount of information available*. The study looked at two sites of wildlife interest in the City, the gardens in Finsbury Circus, and part of the Barbican lakes complex.

The intention of this survey was to assess which species used the two sites, look at the patterns of use of the sites throughout one day, establish what attracts birds to these sites. and compare their uses. Although this is not an in-depth survey of Finsbury Circus or the Barbican lakes, it intends to give an insight into the birdlife of the City.

Method

The survey was carried out one weekday in January 1987. In Finsbury Circus only birds within the confines of the central garden (approximately 7,200 m²) were counted. To have an area of comparable size only one of the lakes (the eastern lake) in the Barbican complex was included in the study, along with the hard surfaces surrounding this lake and an area of short turf to the north of the lake, giving a surface area of approximately 6,600 m².

Each site was surveyed at hourly intervals, Finsbury Circus from 0900 hours to 1600 hours and Barbican Lake from 0930 to 1630 hours, and a count was made of all birds seen during a ten minute period. In Finsbury Circus the count was carried out on a walk around the

* Reports by the London Natural History Society very rarely include information on the City, and the *GLC Wildlife Habitat Survey* (Greater London Council 1985) only surveyed one site in the City due to the size limitations of the survey itself.

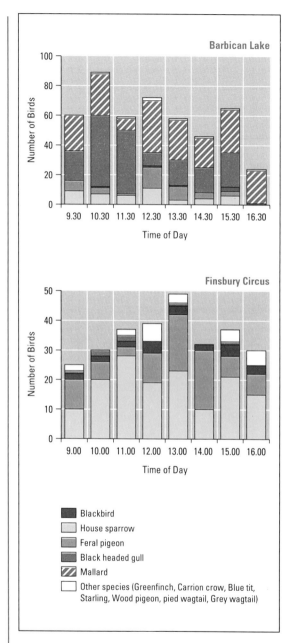

Figure 6.10 The number of birds counted at hourly intervals throughout one day in (a) Finsbury Circus and (b) the Barbican lake area. The other species category included goldfinch, carrion crow, blue tit, starling and wood pigeon in (a) and grey wagtail, pied wagtail and wood pigeon in (b).

garden and in the Barbican the count was made from the high level walkway adjacent to Andrewes House and from the bridge below Gilbert House. Binoculars were used to identify birds at a distance. A note was made of the bird species present, each bird's sex (if possible to identify), the area or habitat in which each bird was seen (on the lake, in a tree, etc.), and each bird's behaviour (feeding, resting, etc.).

Although this is not a foolproof method as birds do not sit still for periods in order that they can be counted, care was taken not to count the same bird twice in one visit and it is hoped that any additions caused by counting a bird twice are balanced by birds missed during the counting period because they were not in view. A ten minute counting period was chosen to ensure that as many birds as possible were counted and because a longer interval would give rise to more repeat counts.

Counts and notes were made throughout the day to see if numbers of birds differed throughout the day, if there was a preference by species for the times of day they visited the areas and if any behaviour patterns could be discerned.

Results

The number of birds seen in Finsbury Circus garden ranged from 25 (at 0900 hours) to 49 (at 1300 hours) (Fig. 6.10a) with an average hourly count of 34.8 birds. Nine species were seen throughout the day but the vast majority of birds present – 86.5% – were house sparrows, feral pigeons and blackbirds. This backs up Douglas's (1983) assertion that only two species are regarded as being typical of built up areas – the house sparrow and the feral pigeon.

These two species and blackbirds were all seen at each count throughout the day. Carrion crows (*Corvus corone*) and blue tits (*Parus caerleus*) were seen in the garden but only high up in the London plane trees. Starlings were mainly seen in the late afternoon and black-headed gulls were only noted flying over.

The greatest number of house sparrows seen was at 1100 hours and at this time they made up 76% of the

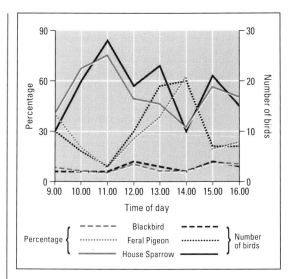

Figure 6.11 The numbers of feral pigeons, house sparrows and blackbirds counted in Finsbury Circus throughout one day in January 1987 and their percentage contributions to the total bird population.

total count. Feral pigeons in Finsbury Circus had their largest percentage of a count at 1400 hours (67%) and their lowest at 1100 hours (9%). The numbers of blackbirds stayed fairly constant throughout the day;

the maximum seen at any one time was 4 (see Fig. 6.11).

The number of birds seen around the Barbican lake ranged from 24 (at 16.30 hours) to 89 (at 10.30 hours) with an average hourly count of 60.4 birds (see Fig.6.10b). Eight species were seen, the majority of the birds counted – 78.7% – being mallard (*Anas platyrhynchos*) and black-headed gulls (*Larus ridibundus*).

Only mallard were seen at every count. Black-headed gulls were not noted after 1530 hours. Feral pigeons and house sparrows were also seen after 1530 hours.

Mallard had their largest percentage of a count at 1630 hours (92%) (although total bird numbers were at their lowest at this time) and were at their lowest at 1130 hours (14%). The numbers of feral pigeons and house sparrows were both at their greatest at 1230 hours; this was the only time people were seen feeding the birds that day.

Figure 6.12 shows the percentages of all birds using the areas/habitats identified in Finsbury Circus and the Barbican throughout the day. The most popular habi-

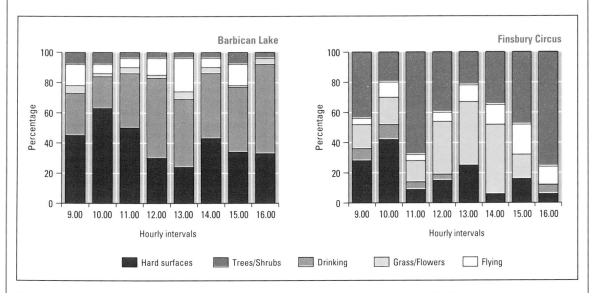

Figure 6.12 Percentages of the total number of birds at each count using the identified locations/substrates in (a) Finsbury Circus and (b) the Barbican lake area at hourly intervals during one day in January 1987. (The trees/shrubs category includes use of the pergola at 1200 at the Barbican lake.)

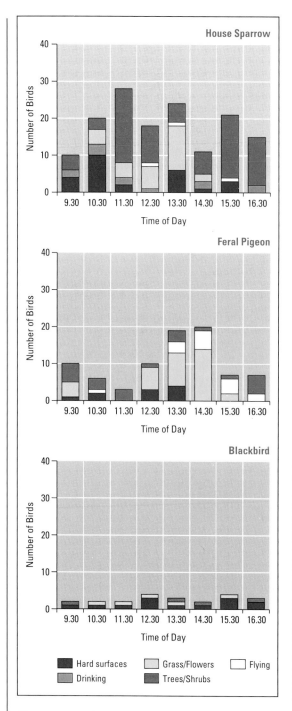

Figure 6.13   The use of habitats in Finsbury Circus by the three most abundant species of bird observed at hourly intervals throughout one day in January 1987.

tats are the shrubberies, trees, hard surface and grass areas. Figure 6.13 show the habitats preferred by house sparrows, feral pigeons, and blackbirds. House sparrows are most commonly found in the shrubberies and on the flower beds and hard surface areas. They were also the only birds seen using the drinking fountain as a water source. Feral pigeons were most often seen in the trees and on the grass areas and blackbirds favoured the pavilion, hard surfaces and grass areas.

At the Barbican lake, the most popular areas were the hard surfaces; these included the terrace of the Guildhall School of Music and Drama, the sunken gardens in the lake and the steps at the eastern end of the lake leading to Brandon Mews. The hard surfaces seemed to be at their most popular in the morning and late afternoon. Also popular was the water itself and many birds, particularly black-headed gulls and feral pigeons, were also seen flying around the area.

The habitat preferences of mallard, black-headed gulls, house sparrows and feral pigeons, the birds most commonly seen at the Barbican, are shown in Fig. 6.14. Not surprisingly, mallard were most commonly found on the water throughout the day with peaks of numbers around lunchtime: 1230 and 1330 hours. Black-headed gulls were seen on the water for six of the eight counts made, although numbers seen on the water at any one time never rose above 18. The hard surface areas were also very popular with the black-headed gulls, their favourite spot being the steps leading to Brandon Mews. House sparrows were mainly seen on hard surface areas in the morning and in the trees and flying around in small groups in the afternoon. Feral pigeons also favoured the hard surface areas and were also often seen flying around the lake area.

Discussion

Although the study area of the Barbican lake was slightly smaller than at Finsbury Circus a greater number of birds were seen at the Barbican throughout the day than at Finsbury Circus. It might be considered that Finsbury Circus, with its greater diversity of habitats and larger size, would be able to support the highest population of birds, but this does not seem to

Plate 6.13 City birds

be the case. The Barbican lake, with its large expanse of open water, attracts high numbers of mallard and black-headed gulls and these species make up most of the birds counted at the Barbican. This situation may, however, change during the summer if the black-headed gulls and mallard move away to breed elsewhere and also higher numbers of people using Finsbury Circus garden during the summer may attract more birds looking for food.

The numbers counted at Finsbury Circus may also be slightly higher than noted as house sparrows, the most commonly found birds in the garden, are very difficult to count accurately when they rest in the shrubs – their favourite habitat there.

The number of birds in Finsbury Circus rose steadily from 25 at 0900 hours to 49 at 1300 hours, falling back to 30 at 1600 hours. The higher numbers seen around lunch-time are probably due to a greater amount of food being available for the birds at this time. Despite the fact that the study was conducted on a chilly, bright but dry winter's day several people were seen eating their lunch in the garden. In summer it is probable that the number of people eating in the garden will be higher, thus attracting greater numbers of birds.

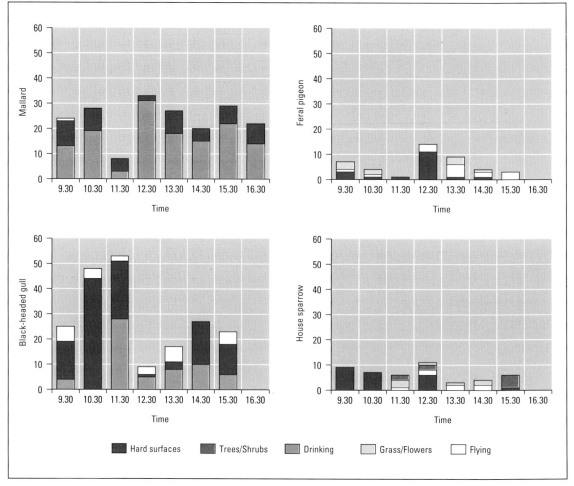

Figure 6.14   Habitat use by the four most abundant species of bird in the Barbican lake area counted at hourly intervals throughout one day in January 1987.

There appears to be a link between the numbers of feral pigeons and house sparrows seen at any one time. When numbers of feral pigeons were at their greatest house sparrow numbers were at their lowest and vice versa (Fig. 6.11). This may be due to the fact that feral pigeons and house sparrows often compete for the same food and that feral pigeons, with their greater size and aggressiveness, are able to win first choice of the food available, the house sparrows only appearing to feed when the feral pigeons move off to rest in their roosting sites outside the garden.

The favourite bird habitats in Finsbury Circus were the shrubberies and plane trees for resting in and the hard surfaces and grass areas for feeding. Also very popular with the house sparrows was the drinking fountain. The relatively low but constant numbers of blackbirds may be explained by the fact that they are highly territorial and the size of an area will limit the number of blackbirds able to use it. Male blackbirds were seen regularly calling and displaying on the roof of the pavilion to the south of the garden.

At the Barbican lake the only birds noted at every count were mallard. From the fact that they were not seen after 1530 it seems that black-headed gulls do not favour the Barbican lake as a night roosting site. Feral pigeons and house sparrows were also not noted after

1530 hours; it is possible that after this time they had gone to their roost sites or moved out of the area altogether. The fact that this lake is surrounded by very tall buildings means that the area gets shaded comparatively early and so bird species such as house sparrows and feral pigeons may move off to other less enclosed areas or settle down to roost earlier than they would in a more open site such as Finsbury Circus. At 1630 hours many mallard were seen settling down on their favourite area – the sunken gardens in the lake.

Although mallard and black-headed gulls both favoured the lake and hard surfaces around it during the day there was very little mixing of the two species (Plate 6.16). Mallard when on the lake were most commonly seen at its western end and gulls at the eastern end. When numbers of gulls on the water rose at 1130 hours the mallard left the study area and moved to the lake outside the conference centre to the west of the study area. In general, though, the gulls kept to the eastern end of the lake.

There was also separation in their use of the hard surface areas. Those favoured by the mallard were the sunken gardens at the western side and the terrace adjacent to these; the black-headed gulls favoured the steps and railings leading up to Brandon Mews at the eastern end of the lake.

Only feral pigeons and house sparrows were seen using the grass area although it is a large space taking up approximately 30% of the study area; the trees in this area were also not very popular.

The numbers of birds seen at the Barbican did not peak, as one might expect, at lunch-time. On this particular day very few people were seen on the terraces around the lake and only two people were seen actually feeding the birds. In the summer no doubt there will be greater opportunities for birds to feed from scraps and left-overs. However, the actual area studied is inaccessible to the general public and this inaccessibility may be the major reason for the mallard and black-headed gulls finding the area so attractive.

Due to time and resource limitations this study has only attempted a simple look at bird life in Finsbury

Circus and the Barbican lake. Further studies could involve studying the sites at different times of the year, studying one or two bird species in much greater detail and assessing if natural food sources are more or less important to birds than those provided deliberately by man.

Conclusion

Despite the hazards of an urban existence and the often hostile attitudes of man towards wildlife, examples of nature in the City of London are abundant. This chapter has quantified and described the major elements of the City's natural systems. In drawing together these elements, it must be noted that the base line for these systems is artificial as the flora of the City is generally planted and intensively managed. However, the green spaces of the City do succeed in attracting wildlife (especially birds), and in a few areas natural colonisation has occurred. Although the different elements studied in this section – vegetational diversity, City trees, and bird life – are interrelated, it is useful to draw conclusions from each survey separately before comparing results and analysing their relationships.

The vegetational diversity of the City's open spaces is influenced by management rather than size (although the larger sites have greater scope for increased diversity), whereas in natural systems the correlation between size and diversity could be expected to be stronger. For similar sized areas, the vegetational diversity of City open spaces is lower than that of natural systems. However, vegetational diversity is only one of a number of factors that contribute towards the value of open spaces in an area such as the City. Nevertheless, there is scope for increasing the vegetational diversity of the City's greenery, which would increase the habitat diversity (especially for native species) and provide more vegetationally interesting open spaces for people.

Although the City has a very high building density and a low vegetational diversity overall, there are many trees present, which add to this diversity – over 70 species being recorded in the survey. Trees are important to the City for a number of reasons as they can function in different ways – socially, physically and for

Plate 6.14   Grey Squirrel

wildlife. Although often taken for granted, trees give pleasure to residents, adding an element of rurality to the built environment, ameliorate the harsh urban climate and provide various habitats for wildlife. City trees can function as habitats singly, (for insects), or in a group as part of a green space (for mammals and birds), or as biological corridors (as street trees do, linking green spaces together). The existence of trees, as with most vegetation, in the City, is due to man's planting, and the urban environment can be very inhospitable. Care must be taken to select healthy, disease-resistant trees of both suitable size and character for the sites available. Effective management saves money in the long term and should concentrate equally on maintenance, the replanting of mature trees, and the enhancement of previously treeless areas. For this, up-to-date tree records must be kept of all trees, their ages, conditions, and also detailed knowledge of species requirements and tolerances. To ensure that trees remain to grace the City, they should be treated as assets and not regarded as liabilities. Their importance in creating a sense of rurality is a major factor in attracting wildlife, so adding to the 'nature value' of the City, trees being more attractive if birdsong is heard, and birds being more attractive in a 'rural' rather than urban setting.

The man-made habitats of the City, and the vegetation planted in them, do attract wildlife, although mainly birds, with a few small rodents. The study of birds in Finsbury Circus and the Barbican shows that birds do find areas of the City attractive. The large expanse of water at the Barbican is popular with mallard and black headed gulls, much of the area being inaccessible to the public so that they are relatively undisturbed; the garden-type habitats of Finsbury Circus attract house sparrows, feral pigeons and blackbirds. The study also noted less commonly seen birds such as grey and pied wagtails (Barbican), and greenfinch, blue tits and carrion crow (Finsbury Circus). Evidence from the survey backs up the idea that birds are attracted to the City by man's waste; Finsbury Circus is most frequented by birds during the lunch period when food is more readily available. This pattern did not occur at the Barbican, indeed few mallard and gulls were seen feeding in the area. An interesting question to answer is where do these birds feed during the winter when few people are around to supply them accidentally or deliberately with food?

When the conclusions of these surveys are put together a pattern for 'nature' present in the City emerges. On one hand there is the well managed, formally planted flora (with a few exceptions), on the other the opportunist scavenging wildlife that lives not on the flora (as it would in a natural environment) but almost exclusively on the scraps and waste left by man. The vegetation no doubt attracts fauna to specific sites but, due to its scavenging nature, the fauna cannot be said to be in the City as a result of the vegetation. The primary attraction for wildlife is the waste; an added bonus is the habitats formed by open space and trees. The City is home to a wide variety of species but the system within which they live is far from natural. Adaptation is the law of urban survival and those species which do not adapt their behaviour soon die out.

Advantages and Disadvantages of Encouraging Wildlife in the City

Encouraging wildlife in the City has both advantages and disadvantages. Most people would like to see a green, more 'natural' City environment. However, by

Plate 6.15   Cleaning park seats

increasing the amount of wildlife, the problems caused (which can be very costly) are also increased.

Vegetation can become physically hazardous. Plants in inappropriate situations can lift paving stones, undermine walls and block access. Damage of this sort can be minimised, if not prevented, by judicious choices of species and site, and problems of light blockage and visual obstruction can be remedied by operations such as crown thinning or crown lifting. Vegetation can also produce hazards – fruits, berries and leaves can become slippery if left on pavements. Lime trees (*Tilia* spp.) are attractive to aphids which, after tapping the phloem of shoots and leaves, extract the sugar and eject the remains as a sticky substance – 'honeydew' – which can be a nuisance to motorists (Owen 1978). Where birds roost physical problems occur – the infestation of buildings or fouling of buildings, pavements, seats and other street furniture (Plate 6.15). This fouling is is a major problem in the open spaces of the City; if it is extensive it can become dangerous, with clean-up costs

running high. The two most common bird species are the feral pigeon and the house sparrow. Both are commensals (they are largely dependent on food provided either accidentally or deliberately by man) and are responsible for most bird problems in the City. Since the beginning of the 20th century, starlings have increasingly used the City for roost sites, but unlike feral pigeons and house sparrows, they move out to the suburbs and rural areas to feed during the day (Thearle 1968). Additional problems are caused by feral pigeons invading and roosting inside buildings, especially when they contaminate food or foul machinery. House sparrows are also attracted into buildings such as canteens, bakeries and food stores.

Many varied attempts have been made to control the populations of feral pigeons and house sparrows in towns, including shooting, trapping and stupefying. Most attempts have had only limited success as areas cleared of birds are quickly recolonised by others from surrounding areas. It may in future be possible to keep

Plate 6.16   Mallard and black-headed gull

population levels to acceptable proportions by inhibiting reproduction but possibly the best way to keep numbers down is to prevent the use of urban areas by these birds. New buildings could be designed to prevent roosting and nesting and many older buildings could be effectively proofed against bird invasions. Prevention would also involve educating the public as to why controls are needed and to encourage them not to feed feral pigeons and house sparrows; some London Underground stations already have notices to this effect. Birds are potential transmitters of disease to man and domestic animals. Feral pigeon droppings have been shown to contain spores of the fungus *Cryptoccus neoformans* which can cause the disease cryptoccosis. Many pigeons and house sparrows are also infected with the disease ornithosis which is transmissible to man. Studies in America by Furcolow *et al* (1961) and Murdock *et al* (1962) have shown a connection between starling droppings and cases of the pulmonary disease histoplasmosis in man.

However, although birds have the potential to transmit diseases to man, there is little evidence to suggest that major problems are caused in this way (Thearle 1968). Of the urban mammals, mice and rats are potentially the most hazardous to man by transmitting diseases and contaminating food. Other disease carriers include insects such as aphids which can transmit fungal, viral and bacterial diseases which may cause extensive physical plant damage and whose control can be very costly in monetary terms.

When encouraging wildlife, it is possible that conditions are created for population explosions of particular species. For example, in 1974 large numbers of vapourer moth caterpillars were found in Berkeley Square; falling from trees, they caused great nuisance to park users, as when handled they can cause an irritating skin rash (Owen 1978). People's attitudes also play a part in deciding whether a particular species is a problem or not; wasps are considered a pest if they sting people, but beneficial when they sting caterpillars (Benson 1981).

People's attitudes are also the basis of most problems associated with smaller non-woody plants. If a plant is labelled a 'weed' it is generally regarded as unsightly and undesirable. Wasteland sites and abandoned gardens are often seen as 'weed-beds' despite the fact that they may be far more interesting and attractive to look at than some formal plantings. Research in this area has been carried out by Cowling (1973), with regard to maintenance of grass verges. This showed that there was an overwhelming preference for short, regular grass with only 15% of those questioned preferring long grass with flowers. Reasons given for liking the short grass included: a neater, tidier appearance; it looks greener; is better for walking and sitting on. It seems that there is a strong expectation within the public for public areas to look 'cared for' (Gilbert 1981).

Although city life can be advantageous to those plants and animals which can exploit the opportunities, there are also great hazards to contend with. Plants must be resistant to trampling, herbicides, pollution and desic-

cation, and natural vegetation needs to be able to compete successfully with the cultivated plants of the City's gardens, whereas animals must contend with hazards such as motor vehicles, poisoning and predation.

Plants and animals are an integral part of urban areas, the City being no exception, although more densely occupied than other similar areas. With more understanding, wildlife could be encouraged in order to benefit both ourselves and the other species concerned. Good management and careful forward planning are needed, however, in order to encourage the 'right' species, and so that populations of species that cause problems in the urban environment can be reduced.

As O'Connor (1981) writes: 'the urban situation provides an opportunity for making nature an immediate experience of most people. By showing them on their doorsteps the interdependence of living things, our society may come to understand better the need for man to exist in harmony with his environment and to conserve its limited natural resources'.

City traffic – noise and congestion

CHAPTER 7

City Open Spaces and Pollution

In recent years increasing attention has been paid to the interaction between plants and pollution. Although the primary thrust of research has been to establish the effects of pollutants on plants, some work has involved the effects of plants on pollution levels. This chapter examines the role of the plants in City green spaces in reducing concentrations of dust particles and noxious fumes, and their effects in cooling the air, adding moisture and reducing noise levels.

Pollution levels in the City vary both daily and annually, dramatic daily variations occuring between peak and low traffic flows, while annual variations include the formation of photochemical pollution during long hot summer spells. Local industrial emissions are not major contributors to the annual mean pollution concentrations of the City; emissions from motor vehicles are of much greater importance.

A major factor which controls pollution levels in the City is the climate, especially wind speed and rainfall. In common with all urban areas the climate of the City is modified by its townscape. These modifications alter the quality of the air and affect its pollution carrying capacity. The funnelling effects of winds in the 'canyon' streets may cause particulate pollution to concentrate in certain local areas (Brown 1983). Rapid water run-off into the sewerage system, and a lack of water capture due to an absence of vegetation, result in reduced evaporation and low relative humidity levels; this increases the air's carrying capacity for dust and particulate pollution and increases the effect of the 'urban heat island' (Chandler 1962). The City also experiences higher average temperatures than outer London due to the heat generated by buildings, people, fuel burning (especially from motor vehicles) and the

high albedo of City construction fabrics such as concrete and asphalt. This temperature difference causes the urban heat island effect which deoxygenates the air and may also cause 'dust-domes' to develop. High temperatures can also lead to a loss of humidity and cause the air to become 'stale'. Temperature inversions may occur due to the modified climate; if a major pollution episode is caught in an inverted layer of cold air the results may be dramatic – the London smogs of the early 1950s were caused by this phenomenon.

These climatic modifications by the townscape and the subsequent changes in the air quality can have serious repercussions on the physical and psychological health of City users. The presence of plants and green spaces in the City is of some importance in ameliorating these effects; not only do green areas help in increasing water catchment and retention to a limited extent in the City, but trees are particularly important as filters, removing many forms of pollution from the air. This chapter looks at six ways in which trees and green spaces can lower the effects of pollution and shows their importance in creating a cleaner urban environment.

Trees, Green Spaces and Particulate Pollution

Much of the air in urban areas consists of very small particles derived from dust, smoke and hydrocarbons which may, under certain climatic influences, give rise to very unpleasant conditions such as the London smog in 1952. Today pollution from smoke has been minimised in the City, and the major source of particulate pollution is motor vehicle exhaust fumes. In combating the effects of such pollutants greenery, particularly trees, can play a significant role by absorbing urban dust.

A mature tree can intercept several hundredweight of dust and the difference in particulate pollution levels between streets with trees and those without can be quite dramatic (with trees 1000-3000 particles per litre of air, without trees 10,000-12,000 particles per litre of air (Brown 1983)). The extent to which a tree can capture dust depends on a number of factors, including the size of canopy, the relative hairiness of the leaves, the roughness of stems and branches, the size of the particles and the windspeed. Table 7.1 indicates the efficiency of particle capture for five species of tree found within the City.

Table 7.1 Data (from Steubing in Duvigneaud *et al* (1975)) to illustrate the capture of particles from the air by five species of shrub found in the City of London.

Species	Lead not retained in air	Deposit of dust (mg)
Ligustrum (privet)	31%	6.0
Lonicera (honeysuckle)	33%	4.0
Carpinus (hornbeam)	36%	3.1
Acer (maple)	39%	3.3
Rosa (rose)	48%	2.3

Seasonality is an important factor affecting particle capture: deciduous trees lose their leaves in autumn, decreasing their capture rate substantially. Although coniferous trees do not lose leaves and are better filters, they are less capable of surviving intense pollution episodes.

Overall measurements of particulate pollution have been carried out by several authors including Lamp (1947) and Hennebo (1955) reffered to in Bernatsky (1975). Table 7.2 uses figures from Frankfurt in 1947, quoted by Bernatsky; they provide a good illustration of how trees and green spaces play an important role in reducing the dust levels in urban environments.

Table 7.2 The relative quantities of dust particles in the air at different locations in Frankfurt and the reduction of this pollution in areas with trees and open spaces.

Site	Particles per unit volume	Percentage reduction of Pollution
Central Station	100.0	0
Town Centre	88.5	11.5
Street (no trees)	65.5	34.5
Avenue (with trees)	20.3	79.7
Town Parks	14.4	85.6

Although no measurements have been carried out in the City of London, it may be assumed that the trend will be similar, as the filtering function of trees is the same in all urban ecosystems.

Trees and the Reduction of Harmful Gas Concentrations

Harmful gases present in the atmosphere include sulphur dioxide (SO_2), nitrous oxides (NO_x) and carbon monoxide (CO). All are associated with urban areas and are usually present as an unwanted by-product of vehicles' internal combustion. Although the plight of trees exposed to acid rain (caused by SO_2) is well-documented, its effects on the City environment can be equally destructive. St Paul's Cathedral had a high rate of erosion almost 8 millimetres per 100 years over the period 1718-1980, and up to 31 millimetres per 100 years at 1980-81 rates (Laxen and Schwar 1985). Both SO_2 and NO_x, as well as being corrosive, are dangerous to the health of people in cities, causing respiratory problems and even death. CO is known to aggravate pre-existing heart conditions (Greater London Council 1983) and to reduce the oxygen carrying capacity of the blood.

These gases are known to cause damage to plants, retarding growth and increasing frost sensitivity in certain species. The effects of vegetation on levels of gaseous atmospheric pollution are less easily defined as both the chemicals involved and their interactions are complex. However, some evidence shows that vegetation can act as a filter for these gases, reducing their concentrations in the atmosphere. Whilst the amounts of absorbed pollutant may be small and dependent on many variables (such as leaf conductance, pollutant concentration and temperature), absorption does take place. The amount of pollutant that a plant can absorb and still survive (the lethal dose) varies between species. Such robust species as London plane and sycamore have long been selected for their ability to withstand high levels of pollution such as those found in cities. Table 7.3 shows the tolerance to pollution from SO_2, ozone (O_3) and fluorine (Fl_2) of the ten most common trees species within the City.

Table 7.3 The levels of tolerance to noxious gas pollution of the ten most common tree species in the City of London (from Beckerson *et al*, 1980).

Rank (1 = most common)	Species	SO$_2$	O$_3$	Fl$_2$
1	London Plane (*Platanus* sp.)	H	H	H
2	Lime (*Tilia* sp.)	M	H	L
3	Cherry (*Prunus* sp.)	H	M	M
4	Maple/Sycamore (*Acer* sp.)	H	H	H
5	Silver Birch (*Betula* sp.)	L	H	L
6	Common Ash (*Fraxinus* sp.)	L	L	L
7	Whitebeam (*Sorbus* sp.)	M	L	M
8	Fir (*Abies*)	H	M	L
9	Beech (*Fagus* sp.)	H	H	M
10	White Willow (*Salix* sp.)	H	H	H

(H = high, M = moderate, L = low)

These species account for nearly 70% of the City's 1860 trees. It can be seen that, apart from the common ash, whitebeam and silver birch, these common species have high tolerances to noxious gas pollution. However, of the saplings recorded in the street tree survey, 15% were *Betula* sp. (silver birch) and 10% were *Sorbus* sp. (whitebeam). Therefore,. 25% of the sapling population in the City has a low tolerance to pollution; this could lead to problems for the City tree population as a whole in the future.

The amounts of noxious gas that a city tree can filter is not insignificant; it has been calculated that a mature tree with a crown volume of 2,700 m^3 and a total leaf surface of 1,600 m^2 could absorb 23 g of SO_2 in an eight hour growing day (Fowler and Cape 1982). As there are nearly 700 mature trees in the City, their combined effect in filtering SO_2 from the air will be considerable. While these calculations make certain assumptions, they do provide a clear indication of how valuable City trees are in absorbing this type of pollution.

Lead Absorption

Lead is a major pollutant in the City, the greatest source being vehicles burning leaded petrol (Greater London Council 1983). Whilst its concentration may decrease in the future due to the introduction of lead-free petrol, it will be a slow reduction in levels and, therefore, an understanding of its present distribution and the damage that it causes is important. Effects of lead pollution can include deficits in intellectual attainment of young children (Greater London Council 1983), hyperactivity and lack of concentration (Newsam 1988). Although widespread throughout the environment, only 10% of body lead is ingested, up to 50% entering the body through the air. Atmospheric lead levels are higher nearer roads, especially those with dense traffic as found in the City.

Atmospheric lead can be filtered from the air by trees – it is deposited on their leaves and then washed off by rain. (Little lead is absorbed through the leaf surface; however, when lead is washed off the leaf into the soil, it may be absorbed through the root system. Therefore, the actual filtering process does not harm the tree immediateley, but side effects such as greater lead concentrations in the soil may have deleterious effects.) The amount of deposition depends on the characteris-

Table 7.4   The quantities of lead found in the leaves of street trees in Brussels (from Mjerus and Denaeyer-de Smèt 1975)

Road/traffic	Situation	Station	Lead level (mg/kg dry matter) in trees
Rue de Fiennes	no vegetation	2	294
±10,000 vehicles/day	no vegetation	3	340
	no vegetation	4	282
Cité Albert 1er Chaussée	adjacent to	8	152
de Mons	green space	9	182
±25,000 vehicles/day	green space	10	129
Rue A Nys	no vegetation	27	34
<5,000 vehicles/day	adj. green space	28	27

tics of the leaf and stem surfaces, the windspeed and other environmental factors. The effect of trees on atmospheric lead levels can be significant, especially in heavy traffic. A study by Denaeyer-de Smèt (1975) showed a reduction of 300mg/kg dry matter of lead in areas where trees were present. The reduction is more marked where the lead levels are very high, such as at roadside verges.

As part of the same survey an analysis of heavy metal pollution levels on two species of tree (*Platanus hispania* and *Robinia pseudoacacia*) in Brussels showed that al-though there is a high correlation between contamination and traffic density (as seen above), green spaces with trees play a significant role in reducing lead pollution (see Table 7.4).

These results show a considerable difference in lead levels between the area next to a green space (stations 8, 9, 10) and an area with less traffic but no trees to filter the air (stations 2, 3, 4). Stations 27 and 28 show that the filtering role of trees seems less effective with low concentrations, there being only a small difference between the green space and adjacent street. The City of London has very high traffic densities, therefore trees and green space should play a significant role in reducing levels of atmospheric lead.

Work carried out by Newsam (1988) in the City of London shows parallels with the Brussels survey in the relationship between traffic density and lead levels. Sites sampled were London Wall, Gresham Street, Lower/Upper Thames Street, Northumberland Alley, Finsbury Circus, Whittington Gardens and the Barbican, with lead levels both on (washings) and within (organic) tree twig samples taken. Figure 7.1 shows the general trend of results: as expected, lead levels rose as traffic density rose. The shielding effect of buildings is well illustrated in the case of the Barbican open spaces, with very low lead levels recorded due to the screening of the open spaces from roads by the complex itself. Buildings also funnel air currents, especially the rows of high buildings (known as 'canyon streets' (Brown 1983)) typical to the

Plate 7.1   Vehicle emission controls could reduce the City's air pollution

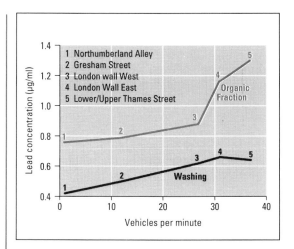

Figure 7.1   Lead contamination in washings from and within tree twig samples taken from five streets in the City of London to illustrate the increase in lead with traffic density (from Newsam, 1988).

City; this can make it harder for airborne particles such as aerosol lead to disperse and may even make them concentrate more. This may be the cause of the very high level recorded in Finsbury Circus which is relatively well screened and traffic-free (although the report suggests that this level is abnormally high). With the presence of so much greenery in Finsbury Circus it could be expected to have very low lead levels in the air; the high concentration found in silver birch is probably due to a build-up of background lead levels after years of filtering. The work shows how much lead can be accumulated by trees, especially the 'washings', that is, lead impacted onto the tree surfaces, the main way in which it is taken from the atmosphere. The report also suggests a saturation point being reached for organic lead at 1.3 mg/ml, although the 'washings' fraction does not appear to be affected. This is important as, although the trees have absorbed as much lead as they are able, they can still act as filters as airborne lead may still be deposited on them. Although the survey highlights the high lead concentrations in the City's trees it serves to show how well they absorb this atmospheric lead, so clearing the urban air.

With the high levels of lead found in the City, the filtering effects of green spaces and trees are undoubtedly important. Although lead is of special importance in the City, other heavy metal dusts are also present in the atmosphere, including cadmium, zinc, copper, arsenic and manganese. These metals, although not in as dangerous concentrations, are still a potential risk to health and are mentioned here since they move in the environment in a similar way and trees are able to ameliorate the problems caused.

The Removal of CO_2 and Replenishment of Oxygen by Plants.

Trees and green spaces play a significant role in the oxygenation of urban areas (in effect the 'cleaning' of the City's air). Due to the heat from the City, convection currents create a heat island effect and a 'dust-dome' develops, where dust from the City's streets 'hangs' in the air over the City. City trees can eliminate these conditions by disrupting the normal convection cycle, providing additional oxygen (from photosynthesis), and introducing cooler fresh air into the City. (Obviously their effectiveness is related to the number of trees present and the area occupied.)

Bernatsky (1975) has calculated that 1 ha of mixed vegetation will have a total leaf area of approximately 5

Table 7.5   Calculated rates of gaseous exchange for six green spaces in the City of London (based on Bernatsky 1975)

Name of Green Space	Area m²	CO_2 absorbed kg/12hr	O_2 emitted kg/12hr
St. Mary Staining	351	315.9	210.6
Stationers Court	557	501.3	334.2
Seething Lane Gardens	842	757.8	505.2
Aldermanbury	904	813.6	542.4
Dunstan-in-the-East Church Garden	1482	1333.8	889.2
Finsbury Circus	7284	6555.6	4370.4

hectares. Such an area could extract 900 kg of CO_2 and release 600 kg of O_2 into the atmosphere in a 12 hour day. An area of 30 to 40 m² occupied by trees supplies the oxygen for the daily requirement of one person (Bernatsky 1975).

Although much depends on the absolute levels of pollution, gaseous exchange levels in the City could look as shown in Table 7.5.

It can be seen that the rate of gaseous exchange increases with the size of the green space. A selection of sizes has been used to give an indication of the differences. Although most green spaces in the City are small (and so their gaseous exchange rates are fairly low), they are probably sufficient in number, when taken together, to make a difference to the overall exchange levels of the City.

This replenishment of free oxygen is important as it decreases the relative amount of polluted air considerably. During a meteorological inversion the mixing of air layers is prevented but a reasonably well-vegetated area can offer local compensation for urban CO_2 output by this emission of O_2. It is this element of gaseous exchange by green space that is often undervalued within the City. The figures indicate that this factor alone is reason enough for their retention.

Humidity and Temperature Regulation

Trees and green spaces create their own microclimate, controlling humidity and temperature in the City. Daily temperature fluctuations are reduced, as shade is provided in daytime and warm air is trapped in tree canopies at night. The cooling capacity of a mature tree is significant. It has been calculated to be 6 million kcal per year (Wang *et al* 1982). This may result in temperature differences of several degrees celsius between vegetated and non-vegetated areas. It has been calculated that the cooling effect of areas in Frankfurt is as much as 3°C (Bernatsky 1960), but due to the smaller area of green space in the City, a rather less dramatic effect is suggested.

Transpiration by vegetation can release large amounts

of water into the atmosphere. This increase in relative humidity can significantly reduce the dust carrying capacity of the air. As a mature tree is capable of transpiring 75-100 gallons of water into the atmosphere on a summer day (Brown 1983), the effects of green space in ameliorating the City's climate are clear.

Open Spaces and Noise Pollution

Urban noise has increased considerably over the last twenty to thirty years. In the City of London, as elsewhere, this noise increase is largely attributable to the increase in the size and volume of motor traffic. In addition (and contributing to this overall increase in noise), there has been a growth in the use of powered machinery particularly associated with building activities and utility operations. Less frequently, helicopters and low flying aircraft further contribute to City noise.

It is accepted that there is a wide variation in human tolerance to the level, duration and types of noise. Most people can tolerate a steady noise at low to medium frequencies while impulsive or percussive noises, and those at high frequencies, are generally recognised as harmful (see Dix 1981). Continuous noise in excess of 70 dB is generally thought to be unacceptable and the noise level set by the GLC Code of Practice in 1984 is

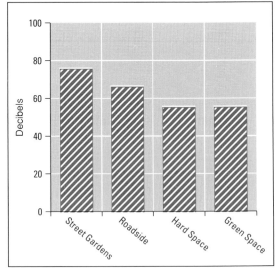

Figure 7.2   Mean noise measurements according to type of open space in the City of London

Table 7.6   Noise levels recorded in City of London open spaces

Site	Type of site*	dB (A)	PN**	Mean dB (A)***
Finsbury Circus	GS	56-64	2.8	60
Moorfields	HS	79-83	1.8	81
St. Dunstan in the East	GS	60-62		61
Cannon St/King William St/ Eastcheap Junction	R	78-88	no reading	83
Wallbrook	R	65	no reading	65
Seething Lane Gardens	GS	58-65		61.5
Fenchurch St Station Forecourt	HS	61-75		68
Blackfriars (road islands)	SG	79-90	1.0	84.5
Temple Gardens (onward from Victoria Embankment)	GS	76	1.8	76
Temple Gardens (onward from Crown Office Road)	GS	56	4.0	56
Elm Court	GS	46	4.6	46
Pilgrim Street	HS	58-62	2.0	60
Amen Court	GS	50	4.5	50
Paternoster Square	HS	56-60	2.0	58
Newgate Street Gardens	GS	68-72	2.0	70
Postman's Park	GS	62-65	2.5	63.5
Little Britain (extremely sheltered section)	GS	50-52	2.9	51
Little Britain	GS	80-82	1.5	81
Barbican (private gardens)	GS	52-54	2.9	53
Barbican (public forecourt)	HS	55	2.8	55

| * | SG = Street Garden | HS = Hard Space | GS = Green Space | R = Roadside |

**   Perceived noise on a semantic scale of 1-5 (the higher the score the less noisy)
***   Three readings were taken at each site from which the means were obtained.

66.5 dB (night time 61.0 dB).

Generally heavy traffic will produce readings in excess of 70 dB at the roadside, while for motor cycles and diesel lorries the figure may exceed 90 dB. At a few metres' distance, powered lawn mowers, pneumatic drills and helicopters on take off and landing will substantially exceed this level. At the other end of the scale, readings in a quiet office or public library would be expected to register noise levels of between 40 and 45 dB.

Figure 7.2 suggests a mean noise figure of 62 dB for a small, but representative, sample of the City's open spaces. They are not 'quiet', but generally acceptable. The figure for street gardens, 84.5 dB, is, as might be expected, considerably higher but more in line with other roadside readings. These means are derived from noise recording details for the twenty open space and roadside sites sampled in the City (Table 7.6). It is interesting to note that the subjective noise survey results (PN), which cover the whole City area, correspond well with the dB meter recordings.

From Table 7.6 it can be seen that some 35% of the sample sites had mean noise readings in excess of the GLC code of practice when types of open space are included. An examination of the location of these sites reveals that they are close to or alongside main traffic routes and that there are no buildings or other effective barriers between the source of the noise and the recording site. The major reasons for the attenuation of noise at the other sites are distance from the source of the noise, that is, main traffic routes and/or the presence of buildings or other barriers which intercept the noise trajectory from its source.

Noise was recorded at five hard space sites. As can be seen from Table 7.6, there is a considerable deviation from the mean for these sites (Fig. 7.2). The Moorfields hard space is extremely busy and very close to two major traffic routes, therefore a high noise level is to be expected. The noise reading for Fenchurch Street Station forecourt hard space is somewhat lower than Moorgate, reflecting the fact that it is generally less busy, while the areas around handle only station traffic*. Paternoster Square has a noise level very similar to the mean which appears to be due to its relative isolation from major traffic noise and the diffusion of pedestrian noise in this large space. The noise level recorded at the Barbican public forecourt is lower than the mean. This site is largely insulated from traffic noise and the reading was made when few people were present.

Noise was recorded at twelve green space sites and, as with the hard space sites, noise levels were determined primarily by distance from traffic noise and with buildings forming barriers to noise transmission. The first point is particularly well illustrated with regard to the largest green space in the City, namely Temple Gardens. A recording of 76 dB was measured close to the boundary of these gardens with the Victoria Embankment (facing northwards away from the traffic). This is considerably higher than the mean noise mea-surement for green spaces. However, another set of recordings was taken, facing inwards, at the northern boundary of the garden adjacent to Crown Office Road, where the noise level was recorded at 56 dB. An attenuation of 20 dB over 140 m is recorded which is in line with other work. The diminution of noise in this instance would have been significantly less had the noise been projected across the same distance of hard surface rather than across soft ground (grass) with additional interception of noise from trees.

The fact that buildings forming noise barriers is well illustrated by the two lowest noise level recordings at Elm Court (46 dB) and Amen Court (50 dB). As the names suggest, these two green spaces are in effect courtyards with buildings surrounding them on all sides and thus they are well insulated from the penetration of exterior noise. A similar reason can be adduced for the relatively

---

* Recorded before present building operations.

lower readings in Postman's Park (Table 7.6).

There are a number of ways in which noise might be reduced in the City's open spaces and indeed within the City generally. The minimising of traffic wherever possible and the exclusion of many heavy vehicles from central areas would help to reduce noise levels although it could well increase noise intensities along and in proximity to the main designated traffic routeways. Pedestrianisation of streets and the separation of people and traffic would also help. Realistically an effort should be made to monitor traffic noise levels in detail and to aim at restraining any increase in traffic noise levels. Further, present regulations with regard to noise control, particularly in sensitive areas, should be rigorously enforced.

There is no doubt that plants do ameliorate noise levels, especially modifying sharp tones (Bernatsky 1975). Under favourable circumstances, with dense planting in parallel rows, with foliage down to the ground and with no gaps, a reduction in noise levels of up to 15 dB may be achieved. Some trees and shrubs are more efficient at reducing noise than others due to variations in their leaf texture (hard leaves being particularly effective), size and density. The shape and size of tree or shrub is also important. Some trees which are most effective in reducing noise levels are *Populus berolinensis, Viburnum lantana, Viburnum rhytidophyllum*, some species of rhododendron, *Tilia platyphyllos* and *Acer pseudo plantanus* (Bernatsky 1975), while among the least successful are *Betula pendula, Crataegus* sp., *Cotoneaster* sp. Partly due to their shape, conifers have only a small effect on reducing noise levels. As might be expected, deciduous trees are considerably less effective during winter and early spring.

Conclusion

From the above examples it can be clearly seen that the greenery of the City, especially the trees, is of great value in the reduction of many types of pollution.

In the case of atmospheric pollution, trees fulfil a dual purpose, not only by filtering pollutants from the air, but also by replenishing it with oxygen, in effect replacing the polluted air with clean air. The filtering of dust and heavy

Plate 7.2

(a) Pollutant gases and acidified rain contribute to erosion and staining of building stone

(b) St. Botolph's, Bishopsgate recently cleaned of grime produced by the City's pollution

metals is a physical process, the particles being impacted onto the leaves and branches and washed off by rain, whereas noxious gases are filtered by absorption into the tree itself. Both processes result in a significant reduction in the levels of unwanted particles in the air, and are of great benefit to the City, both in the reduction of health risks to the population, and in savings on the expensive cleaning and restoration of buildings.

It has also been shown that trees play a significant role in oxygenating the City, especially in the larger green areas such as Finsbury Circus where trees may absorb around 6,555 kg/12 hr of CO_2 and emit 4,370 kg/12 hr of O_2. This is of major importance in such a dense and heavily used area. Not only is the relative amount of pollution decreased but fresh air is provided at the same time, along with effects on the climate such as the stabilization of temperatures and the increase of relative humidity.

To gain the maximum air cleaning effect, as dense a planting as possible commensurate with public use should be aimed for. In public parks and gardens dense groups of trees would be beneficial in removing CO_2 and replacing O_2, whereas along densely trafficked routes added planting would reduce atmospheric lead and noxious gas levels, especially if species are chosen for their efficiency in absorbing pollution and their resistance to pollution damage.

Although the role of plants in reducing noise levels within open spaces in the City is limited, it should not be regarded as insignificant. In the larger open spaces there is scope for a reasonable width of planting of suitable species which will absorb sound through the branches and foliage, with the trunks and heavy branches deflecting it. Areas that would benefit most include Finsbury Circus and Temple Gardens. In the smaller open spaces used for rest and relaxation, visual and sound separation of traffic and people could be achieved at little cost and with minimal redesign if appropriate species were planted. To a limited extent this is being achieved with the continued growth of a beech hedge in Cheapside at the junction of New Change.

Because of the above benefits, wherever possible in redevelopments or the creation of new open space, grass and shrubs with trees are to be preferred to hard surface areas.

Middle Temple Lane

CHAPTER *8*

Case Studies of Open Spaces

Until now in this book we have considered green spaces in terms of their landscape/townscape value, their value for wildlife and their use by people. All these aspects have been discussed separately. In this chapter an attempt is made to consider a number of green spaces taking into account those various aspects and to assess their role within the context of their surroundings. They are each described in turn and their contribution to the adjoining area is considered. The possibility of their enhancement is discussed, on the assumption that each space should provide an area which is as interesting and usable as possible within the limits of economic management, thus suggesting that planting input be orientated towards interesting shrubs, trees and creepers rather than the provision of further labour-intensive flower-beds.

All-Hallows-by-the-Tower Church

The south-east sector of the City is heavily built up, with very little obvious open space of any description. Part of its eastern side has been shown (Corporation of London 1978c) to be more than a quarter of a mile from the nearest open space to which the public has ready access. Those open spaces which do exist are all very small and some of them are closed outside normal working hours. However, beyond the south-east boundary lie the open spaces of Trinity Square Gardens, Tower Hill and the Tower of London (with its attendant crowds of tourists), which, to some extent, relieve the overall shortage of this area of the City.

All-Hallows-by-the-Tower church, rebuilt since the Second World War, has a conspicuous location, visible both from the east by being elevated above

Tower Hill, and from the west across the wide bend of Great Tower Street and Byward Street. The green space lies on the east side of the church, forming a small churchyard (approximately 12.5 m x 40.5 m).

The churchyard consists of two lawns with flowers, shrubs and limited tree planting (Plate 8.1) which serve to distinguish this area. It is not open to the public. It relates more to the church and provides a landscaped setting for its eastern end. Unfortunately, as the entrance to the church is on the far side of the building, the churchyard does not provide an approach to the church. However, the *Robinia* trees on the north side provide some welcome greenery in Byward Street, and thereby enhance the street scene.

Tower Hill, All-Hallows

The area immediately to the east of All-Hallows churchyard is undergoing redevelopment. Previously the area comprised a hard, bleak and open paved terrace, with very little to distinguish it, laid out on the top of a basement structure. The restoration is predicated on strengthening the basement structure. Immediately adjacent to Tower Hill itself and 'coordinated' with it in terms of floorscape two not unattractive hard cobbled open areas, demarkated by low walls and railings have been laid out. They are separated from each other by a wide flight of steps down to Tower Hill and to the basement area beneath, which is occupied by a McDonald's resturant, strategically placed for the Tower trade, the entrance to which is covered by a rather unprepossessing arched glass sheeted roof.

Plate 8.1   All-Hallows-by-the-Tower Churchyard (before redevelopment).

Between this recently redeveloped area and All-Hallows churchyard it is proposed to create a paved garden, necessary because of the anticipated heavy use by tourists, with a number of fine standing planters. Seating will also be provided. Although providing good views of the Tower, it is thought that much of this area's attractiveness will be created by its openness. However, it would be advantageous to screen the site from road traffic noise and general openness to the north by extensive shrub hedge planting, emphasising separation between traffic and a pedestrian area. It would also make the most of its southerly aspect.

Tower Place

To the west and to the south of All-Hallows church is a large, hard and fragmented open space known collectively as Tower Place (Plate 8.2). It comprises firstly the 'churchyard' immediately to the west of the church building itself, which is distinguished from

the other areas by a floorscape composed of granite sets; all other parts of Tower Place have a rather undistinguished floorscape of grey paving stones. Secondly there is a lengthy central sector adjacent to the church on the north and unattractive office buildings of the 1960s and early 1970s on the south. Opposite the 'churchyard' a courtyard to the Bowing Building opens off the central sector. To the southeast, after traversing a covered sector formed by the buildings, access is gained to a banal hard space in the form of a courtyard whose sole redeeming feature lies in the views which may be had towards the River Thames.

Unfortunately, both as a result of the vacuous and deteriorating nature of these buildings and the overall impression of bleakness created by large areas of monotonous floorscape, these areas as a whole are hardly attractive. The Bowing courtyard has a number of small poorly maintained planters and a poorly sited and displayed statue, 'The Hammer Thrower', by

Plate 8.2   Tower Place – All Hallows

John Robinson (1973). The southeastern court is in a state of disrepair with little to recommend it. The central area has some positive features, including a number of mature trees including plane, cherry and a beach tree, while adjacent to the 'entrance' to this hard space from Byford Street are two well stocked and tended brick planters.

However, this area has considerable potential for improvement. It has a prime location while being relatively isolated from traffic noise and the immediate pedestrian crush around Tower Hill itself. A number of relatively inexpensive changes could be made to improve the attractiveness of the space to potential users. The amount of hard space should be reduced overall and broken down into smaller areas. Extensive planting probably would be difficult due to subsurface structures and underground services. It is therefore suggested that attention be given to varying its paving design and incorporating small grassed sections to reduce the monotony. Large, well de-

signed and substantial tubs or planters, perhaps similar to the present successful ones nearby, could be filled with shrubs and creepers, the latter trained onto pergolas and onto the church building in order to provide vertical interest apart from the trees. Creepers could also be effectively used should the present office buildings be refaced (or rebuilt). Another feature which could be more fully exploited is the view of the Tower, which is well focused by the relatively narrow central sector which extends visually toward the Tower and is bounded by the length of the church and office buildings.

Overall this complex of hard open spaces should be highly valued, given its proximity to the 'honeypot' of the Tower. What is needed is an integrated framework for renovating the area as a whole which is sensitive yet alive to the opportunities offered by its location, emphasising its own diverse elements at the same time providing shelter from bad weather to cater for year round use.

Plate 8.3

Seething Lane
Garden

Seething Lane

This long narrow island (approximately 72 m x 12,5 m) of greenery with streets on three sides and a private car park to the east, is quite unlike the previous green space at All-Hallows in that it is away from the main road, tucked amongst high buildings, with the Port of London Authority Building to the east and Corn Exchange Chambers to the west. It is also unlike All-Hallows in that it is not hidden behind a wall but separated from the street only by railings. It can therefore be enjoyed from adjacent streets (Plate 8.3) without the necessity of actually entering it.

It is essentially a garden with an extensive lawn at the south end surrounded by flower beds and young trees, many of which are labelled. The north end has a more mature selection of large trees and shrubs, and is therefore comparatively shady in summer (Plate 8.4). There is only one point of access, mid-way along the

Seething Lane frontage; this is gated and closed in the evenings and at weekends. There are a number of seats and rather visible rubbish bins at strategic locations.

This green space serves as a miniature square, an island of greenery in a densely built-up area. The trees and shrubs overhang the streets (Plate 8.3) and provide a foil for the hard outline of the buildings. They also serve as a home for birds (Fig. 8.2), supply oxygen to the atmosphere and filter dust from the air. In summer the grey streets are enlivened with a wonderful variety of greens, from the light green of the *Robinia* to the dark green cypresses. Figure 8.2 shows that this garden, in spite of its small size, contains a far greater number and variety of trees than All-Hallows or St. Olave's Churchyard which are in the same area.

The rich variety of plants has created a sense of enclosure within the gardens and affords people some privacy from being overlooked from adjoining buildings (Plate 8.4). However, it is unable to exclude the noise

Plate 8.4   Seething Lane Garden

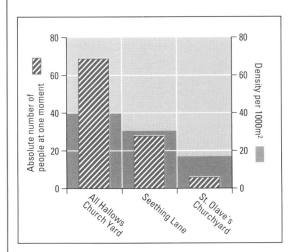

Figure 8.1   The number of people counted at one moment (open columns) in a sunny summer lunchtime in three case-study areas, and their density per 1000 m² (shaded columns)

of passing aircraft and helicopters, which tends to echo between the high buildings. In addition, the occasional passing road vehicle intrudes into the peace of the garden, particularly as nowhere is more than a few feet from the road.

Unfortunately, because this garden is away from the main thoroughfares, it is little used except during lunch-times in good weather when it can become crowded with office workers (Fig. 8.1). This is in spite of its location only some 180 metres from the crowds on Tower Hill. However, because of this it can be a refreshingly quiet place in which to relax, as several vagrants have discovered.

Unlike All-Hallows, there appears to be little scope for improvement other than the need for some sign-posting from Tower Hill and Byward Street to advertise its presence. It would, for instance, provide some tourists with a welcomed break from the 'honeypot' of the Tower of London, although the capacity of Seething

Lane is very limited. To be beneficial to tourists the garden would have to be open at weekends and into the evenings in the summer, which it is not at present. This would increase the problem already experienced of attracting vagrants, although this may partly be due to underutilisation at present.

It is also suggested that thicker shrub planting around the edge, or less drastic pruning of the existing shrubs would help to minimise the intrusion of activity in the street.

St Olave's Churchyard

This is a tiny (approximately 22 m x 16 m) churchyard maintained by the Corporation of London almost opposite the Seething Lane garden described above. It is completely enclosed by buildings on three sides and a 1.5 metre high wall on the road frontage topped with railings. Yet, in spite of this, it contains a variety of trees, shrubs, bedding plants and bird life, as shown in Fig. 8.2. It therefore, in a way, combines the luxuriant vegetation of the Seething Lane garden with the detachment from its surroundings of All-Hallows.

Like All-Hallows the churchyard has to be entered to be appreciated, although its tall trees advertise its presence from Pepys Street opposite (Plate 8.5). The trees are arranged around the edge of the yard, with a path around the centre linking the single entrance gate with the church and with several seats. In the centre is a small lawn with a few gravestones, around which is set a colourful display of bedding plants.

This green space serves as a graveyard and as a setting for the church, and also as a light-well for the adjacent office buildings. Because of the latter it is heavily overlooked, but the buildings themselves and the wall on the road frontage serve to exclude most extraneous noise. The yard is therefore the most peaceful of the green spaces in the area, with most noise coming from a colony of house sparrows and from air-conditioning units in the offices; one can almost forget the activity in Seething Lane and Pepys Street.

Other than opening up a vista of the church from the

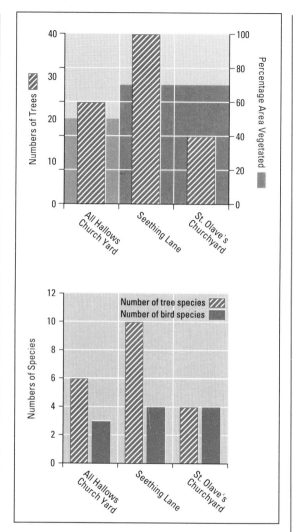

Figure 8.2   (a) The number of trees and the percentage of the area vegetated and (b) the number of species of birds and trees in three case-study open spaces

gateway, this green area contributes little to the townscape of the area. Although the trees in it are visible from Pepys Street, they are subordinate to those in the Seething Lane open space (Plate 8.5). However, this space does enrich the area, providing a surprising enclave amongst the large office buildings, and a quiet haven for wildlife.

As with the Seething Lane garden, this churchyard is little used except by office workers for lunch-time

Plate 8.5   Turnagain Lane

relaxation in the summer and as a thoroughfare to the church. The trees and high buildings give extensive shade, but the centre of the yard makes a pleasant sitting area. The high wall at the front tends to make the yard appear semi-private, which may restrict its use still further; no vagrants, for example, have been observed here. There appears little scope for improvement other than limited sign-posting for those unfamiliar with the area. One or two shrubs were dying at the time of the survey and needed replacement.

Discussion

Figures 8.1 and 8.2 demonstrate the contrast between the extensive area of All-Hallows churchyard, with its low figures for vegetation and birdlife, and the smaller green area in Seething Lane, with its greater amount of vegetation and birdlife. In the survey Seething Lane appeared more attractive, tidy, harmonious and generally more 'rural' than the churchyard, in spite of its

awkward shape and the proximity of roads and buildings.

Noise was perceived as a problem at all sites in the south-east sector of the City, particularly at the most popular ones. The noise came principally from road traffic, aircraft and helicopters, but also from air-conditioning units (St Olave's churchyard) and building operations. Whilst the continuous roar of traffic was annoying in All-Hallows Churchyard, the lower level around Seething Lane was rated as a similar problem, as it was intermittent and therefore more noticeable.

Figure 8.1 shows the number of people counted at one time on a hot day at lunch-time in these areas. Again All-Hallows churchyard stands out as most popular, presumably due to its conspicuous location on a main road opposite the Tower of London. The seating capacity of Seething Lane and St Olave's churchyard is limited, yet Seething Lane was extremely popular bearing in mind its back-street location and the fact that nobody could go on the lawn during the survey because a sprinkler was in use.

The main activities noted in these areas were, not surprisingly, resting, eating, drinking, reading and chatting with friends. Other regular occurrences were people feeding the birds, sunbathing, and, unfortunately, vagrants rummaging in rubbish bins. St Olave's churchyard also had several people passing through it to the church. Although one cannot walk through the gardens in Seething Lane, they are easily appreciated from the street whereas All-Hallows churchyard is more detached, nevertheless it is used as a resting place for tourists.

Several vagrants were noted during the survey and they became more noticeable during periods of low general usage. They may tend to discourage people from using the open spaces at these times and thereby accentuate the 'peaking of use' at lunch-times. This peaking is also accentuated by the closure of the Seething Lane garden in the evenings and at weekends; it is virtually just a garden for the offices. The two churchyards stay open longer as they are controlled by the church authorities. The closure of these spaces is unfortunate, but is probably necessary to protect them from vandalism.

Thus, the main functions of the open spaces in this part of the City of London are, in descending order of importance:

- as resting areas for picnicking, meeting friends and waiting;

- to form features in the townscape and settings for buildings;

- to form a reservoir of plants and wildlife, to supply oxygen for the atmosphere and to extract dust from the air.

The greatest scope for improvement lies in the area around All-Hallows church, Tower Hill and Tower Place which, valued together provide a considerable area of open space.

The Seething Lane and St. Olave's churchyard gardens are highly regarded but little can be done to reduce the intrusion of traffic noise here apart from denser shrub planting on their edges.

*   *   *   *   *

In contrast to the south-east sector, there are a considerable number of open spaces in the central western sector of the City, and almost nowhere is more than 400 metres from an open space to which the public has access (City Background Study 1978c). There are, additionally, a number of spaces which are not open to the public. Also unlike the south-east sector, located mainly in the core of the City, there are a number of large open spaces, for instance, St. Paul's Churchyard, Postman's Park, Paternoster Square and Newgate Street Garden, Greyfriars. This is fortunate since this area has a considerable tourist and commuter population. There is, however, a wide disparity in the extent to which these spaces are used. Not surprisingly, St. Paul's Churchyard is popular but others are much less well known.

Turnagain Lane

This small open space is located between 34 Farringdon Street and 21 Holborn Viaduct, opposite Standard House (56-58 Farringdon Street). Essentially of triangular shape, it stretches over approximately 15 metres between Turnagain Lane and 21 Holborn Viaduct.

The space is slightly elevated near Turnagain Lane and paved over completely, save for a raised bed containing small shrubs and an apple tree. A low wall and a line of three young planes screen the area from the street. Access is via three steps from the corner of Farringdon Street/Turnagain Lane and beside Holborn Viaduct. Presently no seats or rubbish bins are provided, the former apparently having been removed. The space itself is bleak, uninviting and in a poor state of repair. The design of the raised bed is sterile and the amount of greenery too small to dominate the area, while the large reflecting windows of 27 Holborn Viaduct and the design of Standard House give the space an exposed and impersonal feeling. The raised bed and walls are an effective screen for the parking facility of 21 Holborn

Plate 8.6   Turnagain Lane

Viaduct (see Plate 8.6). The paved area is not inviting.

The local significance of the space lies in the fact that it affords some room for greenery in an otherwise barren Farringdon Street (Plate 8.7). The major contribution is made by the line of London planes which are almost in the street itself, the only trees between Ludgate Circus and Holborn Viaduct. The open space itself has the character of a forecourt and makes no appreciable contribution. Use of this space is limited, by virtue of its design and location, to the level of a cosmetic enhancement of a largely sterile environment. It may occasionally be used as a rest area, but with noise levels in excess of 70 dB, and with no seating provision, it scarcely invites use by the public.

The size of the space, the close proximity of a busy secondary road and its enclosure by relatively featureless tall buildings leave little room for improvements.

The planting of a fast-growing tree such as *Tilia cordata*

Plate 8.7   Farringdon Street (Turnagain Lane on left)

'Greenspire' towards the back of the paved area would ameliorate the lack of trees in this part of the City. Additional shrubs alongside the windows of 21 Holborn Viaduct and the adjoining wall would create greater intimacy. Provision of two or three wooden benches would allow the space to be used as an occasional resting place. The central plane in the front of the space will have to be removed as the group reaches maturity. A tree at the back of the open space which can compete in size without presenting a similar spread of crown

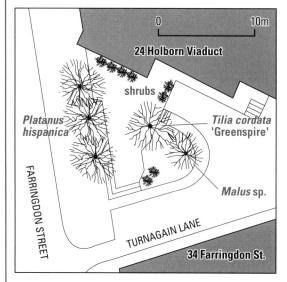

Figure 8.3   Suggested improvements for the small open space in Turnagain Lane.

would balance the existing trees. It is suggested that the *Malus* sp. growing in the raised bed be retained until such time.

Newgate Street Garden

This open space lies on the northern side of Newgate Street at the approach to the junction with King Edward Street. It consists of three presently discrete areas, lying to the west of the ruins of Christ Church Greyfriars and the recently renovated Vestry House: an enclosed green area, an adjoining hard surface area flanking Newgate Street and a small bed of shrubs adjacent to the south end of the Vestry House. The total open space area is approximately 1,000 m².

Plate 8.8   Newgate Street Garden

The green space, part of an earlier burial area, consists of two grassed areas separated by a central hard surface path (Plate 8.8). There are numerous small shrubs and trees along the boundary of this area with the post office, while a hedge of shrubs and small trees separates it from the hard surface space along its southern boundary. The entrance to the green space is in Greyfriars Passage and the street boundary line is dominated by iron railings and the entrance gates. The opposite (western) boundary consists mainly of unsightly building frontage. This is particularly unfortunate as it is the main focus for visitors entering the space which is itself dominated by several large trees whose canopies tend to overshade the area. Seats (and litter bins) are provided each side of the pathway and the all too prevalent bird droppings further diminish the public value of this space.

The adjoining hard surface area consists of a slightly elevated (from street level) paved section partially surrounded by a low bush wall on the western side. There are a number of randomly positioned benches generally facing Newgate Street. There are litter bins and some plant tubs. The overall impression is not very attractive.

The small shrub bed occupies the space between Vestry House and a part of the Christ Church wall and the pavement flanking Newgate Street from which it is

Plate 8.9   Newgate Street Garden *c* 1969

separated by a low open wooden fence. Visually it is not particularly appealing (Plate 8.9).

The original association of this green space with Christ Church is evidenced by the entrance being in Greyfriars Passage rather than in Newgate Street, showing an access between the church and present green space. This is further supported by the remaining headstones to be found within the space, attesting to its earlier use as a burial ground. Today the green space is open to the public, providing some degree of seclusion from Newgate Street itself, although the overall noise level is rather high. The adjoining hard surface area was originally the site of a row of tenements dating back to the fourteenth century (Lloyd 1979). At the present time the area is provided with seats and frequently used by people waiting for buses at the nearby stop in Newgate Street. The small shrub bed adjacent to Vestry House contains a variety of species.

From general observation it appears that the green space area is little used by the public for rest and relaxation although there are a number of offices and other places of employment in the vicinity (nearly 9,000 people pass through St. Paul's underground station every morning) and it is adjacent to the Paternoster shopping area as defined in the *Pedestrian Movement Survey* (1969). Its principle use is that of a not altogether successful visual foil to the surrounding buildings. As might be expected the public make far greater use of the seating facilities of the adjacent hard surface area, open as it is to Newgate itself, while the adjoining bus stop obviously increases the numbers substantially (Transport and Environment Studies 1985).

Four changes would secure both the integration of two major open spaces and encourage more passers-by to use them. Firstly, the partial renewal of the shrub and small tree hedge which follow the present boundary between the 'green' and 'hard' spaces. Secondly, the closure of the present gateway in Greyfriars Passage

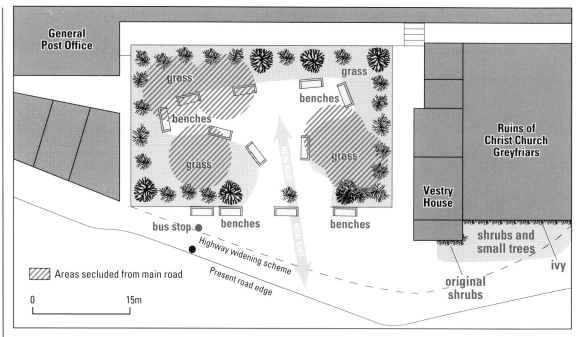

Figure 8.4   Suggested improvements to Newgate Street Garden.

and its incorporation in a redesigned boundary to encourage the feeling of enclosure. Thirdly, a change of access to entice people into the area from Newgate Street (Fig. 8.4). This would also involve the removal of the semi-established tree on the south side of the present green space as well as lightening a central area. This would create a wide and informal entrance to the area. Fourthly, using the small trees and shrubs already removed, together with new stock, the planting up of both the eastern and western boundaries should be undertaken. This is particularly important on the western side as a visual foil to the nondescript buildings abutting the green space. Essentially, two separate and inter-related areas would be created, with the hard surface area remaining for immediate use by pavement traffic while the wide informal entrance to the green area from this hard apron would provide a useful, informal and more secluded resting area.

The new southern boundary of this integrated open space will not conflict with highway widening plans (Corporation of London 1986) which will considerably reduce the present hard surface area. Unfortunately the road widening scheme will reduce the area of the small shrub bed and

it would be sensible to plant here a more limited area adjacent to the building line in order to achieve the greatest possible greening effect in the limited area which will remain.

The creation of a new access for this area would facilitate greater use of this green space at the same time as providing pleasing views towards a part of St. Paul's Cathedral to Newgate Street itself, as well as an angled view to the pleasantly restored Vestry House, while maintaining an appropriate degree of separation from the street itself.

*   *   *   *   *

The Inns of Court

The Inns of Court lie in the south western corner of the City, immediately to the south of Fleet Street, with their southern boundary on the Victoria Embankment. Parts of the complex form the largest 'closed' green space in the City (City of London Polytechnic Survey: see Chapter 3): these are the Inner and Middle Temple gardens, with an area of 16,879 m². The area also consists of a number of 'courts', either hard or green open spaces surrounded by the Temple buildings. Although there is public access, the area is privately owned, and this is reflected in the general atmosphere of the Temple. The overall effect has been compared to the precinct character typical of the older Oxford and Cambridge colleges, making it one of the most valuable and enjoyable enclaves in central London. The area functions as a minor tourist attraction; it is estimated that there are 100 visitors per day to the Temple church (Corporation of London 1976).

The Temple developed from the medieval establishment of the Knights Templar, but the only surviving feature from this period is the Temple church (c.1160-5). The Middle Temple Hall dates from Elizabethan times and the present complex was largely built in the late 17th century. Although classically designed in red-brick 3 or 4 storey blocks (c.1670-1700), 19th century rebuilding has altered the original style. The Temple suffered heavy bomb damage during the blitz, including the loss of the Lamb building (Bacon c1946), and much restoration and rebuilding work occurred after the Second World War.

Although there are a number of open spaces in the vicinity of the Temple, including those in Fetter Lane, New Fetter Lane, and at St Bride's churchyard, they are all small hard spaces. In addition, with the exception of St Brides, they are all roadside open spaces, so that the Inns of Court are the only well-screened quiet enclaves in this part of the City.

Because of their 'private' atmosphere and the gates at the entrances, the open spaces of the Temple are little used for relaxation by the local office workers from outside the complex. They are, however, used as pedestrian thoroughfares by workers within the Temple, with occasional use as lunch spots during the summer. Some of the courts, such as King's Bench Walk, Brick Court and Essex Court, are used for car parking, which is not consistent with their use as open space. However, it must be noted that they are privately owned and that there is a general lack of parking facilities in the City. As the Temple is a minor tourist attraction, it is likely that recreational use of the courts will be popular among tourists, especially during the summer months when they make ideal resting places.

Although the Inns of Court are rare examples of 17th century architecture in the City, the effect of the buildings themselves has been described as 'rather mediocre' (Lloyd, 1979), and that it is the relationship of the buildings to the open spaces, the landscaping, and the subtle changes in levels that give the superb total effect. The whole of the Temple area therefore provides an excellent example of how open spaces can characterise the architecture of the townscape.

Three courts within the Temple have been studied in greater detail: Church Court, Fountain Court and Elm Court. These highlight the intimate and private quality of the Inns of Court yet show the great variations to be found among the various courts.

Church Court

This was originally the site of the Lamb building, destroyed during the Second World War. The total area of the court is 1,200 m². It lies to the south of the Temple church and the Masters Garden, its border to the east is the Francis Taylor building, to the west the Farrars building and cloisters, and to the south, the Inner Temple Hall and Library. The whole area of the court is paved and although litter bins are provided, there are no seats. The court is enclosed on all sides, access being through an archway from King's Bench Walk at the eastern end, and from Inner Temple Lane to the west. Despite this enclosure the paved surface is vacuous and lacks intimacy, so the space appears barren, which is accentuated by the lack of distinguishing features.

The court serves primarily as a pedestrian thoroughfare between the various annexes of the Inns of Court. Although some of the hard surface courts are used as car parks, Church Court is not and so is a valuable hard space. However, its appearance does little to enhance the surrounding buildings or contribute to the overall character of the Temple area. Except for a small area of shrubs adjoining the Masters Garden, the court is devoid of vegetation and contrasts noticeably with the other two courts surveyed, Elm Court and Fountain Court. Nevertheless there is a sense of tranquility within Church Court due to the surrounding buildings screening out much of the City noise. The small

Plate 8.10   Church Court

alleyways and the cloisters help to create a collegiate atmosphere.

Pedestrians ferquently use the Court passing between King's Bench Walk and the adjoining courts to the west. Occasionally the court is used at lunchtimes, with informal seating provided along the length of step adjacent to the Temple Church.

Church Court offers potential for the fundamental redesigning of an open space (Fig. 8.5). This would increase the value of the site in relation to the surrounding buildings while perpetuating the 'collegiate' feeling of the Inns of Court in general. This would not necessarily interfere with its primary role as a walkway, and would add to the visual pleasure of the people using it as such.

The provision of a focal point in this space would be a major improvement, as it could reduce the vacuous feeling and the barrenness of the area. The two circular

pavement details present do not work; being barely noticeable, they do not break up the paved floorscape as intended. However, if these were used as the sites for two fountains, each surrounded by a small circle of grass and a low fence, the monotony of the paved area could be broken up successfully. The diameter of each feature could be up to 6 m without any interference to pedestrian movement. As well as the fountains forming a focal point, the sound of water would further divorce the court from the noise of the City, so enhancing the atmosphere.

The surface must remain paved so that the court is protected from the effects of its heavy pedestrian use. However, the use of different shaded stones set in patterns may improve the overall appearance of the floorscape. If possible a flower border or small shrubs should be planted on the south side of the court, although they will have to be carefully sited to avoid reducing access, and blocking light from the ground level windows.

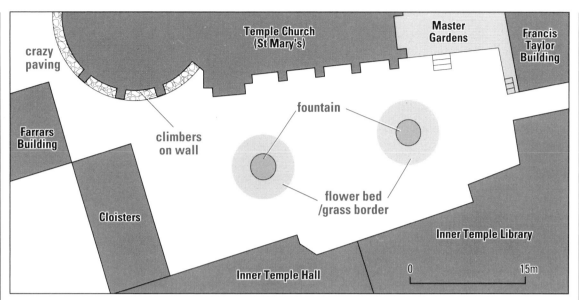

Figure 8.5   Suggested improvements to Church Court

The eastern end of the court is most successful due to the climbers and shrub border adjoining the Masters Garden. This should be mirrored at the western part of the court around the alcoves near the entrance of the Temple Church. In addition, the floorscape of these alcoves could be changed to grass or gravel with a small kerb divider from the main court, or alternatively, crazy-paved as has been done on the north side of the church. The more central alcoves should be left for informal seating, although strategically placed planters could help to break up the stark walls.

As a means to remedy the shortage of seating in the Inns of Court generally, benches could be provided for workers or tourists, either along the north or south side of the court. However, it is recognised that the court is under private ownership and that there may not necessarily be the willingness overtly to encourage greater public use.

These recommendations will not interfere with the court's primary function as a walkway, but should add much to its visual aesthetics, forming a continuum of greenery between the adjoining Pump Court and Elm Court, and so developing a greater sense of unity for the Inns of Court as a whole.

Fountain Court

This court lies on the western boundary of the Temple and, although of roughly the same area as Church Court, has a completely different character. It is of irregular *L* shape, lying to the north of Middle Temple Hall, with access from Middle Temple gardens to the south, Middle Temple Lane from the east and New Court from the north. The space is enclosed, being surrounded by three and four storey buildings; however, there is a break on the south side, with steps leading down to the Middle Temple gardens and the Victoria Embankment.

The court is hard surfaced, with gravel, crossed by paved footpaths, with a small paved area adjoining the Middle Temple Hall. There are eight trees in the court, four large planes, and four smaller laburnums, a horse chestnut, and an American lime around a small fountain that gives the court its name. The building to the west of the area has two small planters with flowers at its entrance, a small lawned area with shrubs, and climbers growing on the walls. Close to the steps to Middle Temple Garden on the south side is a small hedge. Positioned around the fountain are three benches with litter bins. The atmosphere is essentially private,

Plate 8.11   Fountain Court

as it is almost completely enclosed, however, it is more informal than some of the other courts, due to the seating and trees around the fountain which give a feeling of intimacy rather than formality. The court is very quiet due to its enclosure and its position within the Temple complex.

While the court has a secondary function as a seating area, its principle function is that of a thoroughfare, forming a link between New Court, Temple Lane and the Middle Temple Hall. It also serves as a forecourt to the latter, the entrance to which is in the south eastern corner of the court. The seating around the fountain appeared well used, although only by workers in the complex and only for very short times. This court is significant as it provides the only intimate seating area in the Temple, with a fountain and a view over the Thames. Architecturally the court functions as a welcome break from the other more formal courts and the informal layout of trees gives it a high feeling of rurality.

Although at present forming an attractive rural oasis, there is some scope for minor improvements to Fountain Court which would not change the informal character but rather enhance it (Fig. 8.6).

The inclusion of more grassed area could break up the floorscape, adding interest. Although the gravel surface is much more aesthetically pleasing than the large expanse of paving stones at Church Court, it is rather monotonous and looks unkempt, with grasses and weeds growing up through it. The paved footpaths should be retained as they add character to the area, providing a different shape within the larger *L* shape. The paved area adjacent to Middle Temple Hall looks out of place in the court, especially as it serves no real function. This could be remedied by either an extension of the gravel surface over this area or the creation of a new small lawn area.

The walls of the building on the north side of the court look rather bare. Some climbers on these walls would

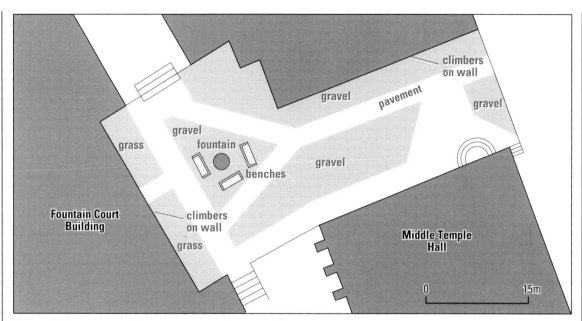

Figure 8.6   Suggested improvements to Fountain Court

break up the red-brick surface and add visual interest. On this building, too, there is access to electricity cables and ventilation units which distract from the rural atmosphere and could be quite simply masked by the strategic planting of a shrub border or alternatively by growing more climbers on the walls. However, care would have to be taken not to block light from the ground level windows.

The fountain, although an attractive feature, looks rather unkempt, with only a few water plants. Either these should be removed, or more should be added and their management intennsified, to add to the feature rather than detract, as is the present case.

This court is generally litter-free and tidy. Although Fountain Court is one of the more 'rural' courts, there may be problems in the future as the age structure of the trees is unbalanced. Young trees must be planted so that they can become established and eventually take over from the mature ones that are present now.

Elm Court

Elm Court lies in the centre of the Temple area, to the east of Fountain Court, on the opposite side of Middle

Temple Lane. To the west is the Lamb building, while Inner Temple Hall lies to the east. The court has access from Middle Temple Lane to the west, from The Terrace to the east, and from Crown Office Row to the south. It is made up of a number of distinct features on two levels. The northern part consists of a rectangular paved area with a smaller inset grass area surrounded by a low iron railing and containing a flower bed, two almond trees, one linden and two horse chestnuts. To the south is a lower level reached by steps at the eastern and western ends of the court. This is a long narrow paved area, along the northern section of which is a raised bed with shrubs and flowers 'linking' it to the higher area.

The court has no seating and no litter bins. The atmosphere of the court, like the others, is secluded but as it is overlooked on all sides by buildings and has no seating, one feels compelled to hurry through it, there being no reason to relax and enjoy the area.

Like most of the courts, Elm Court functions primarily as a thoroughfare. Its use as a pedestrian routeway is important due to its central location and its proximity to car parking facilities at King's Bench Walk. Although the court is well landscaped and contains

Plate 8.12   Elm Court, building works in progress

interesting features, there are no provisions for relaxation so that it cannot easily be used for any other purpose. The court plays an important architectural role, the grassed central area acting as a break to the harsh wall and floor materials, in direct contrast to Church Court where the paved floorscape simply increases the monotony of the area. The court functions on a purely visual basis as there is no access to the central lawn and no furniture. However, the visual pleasure gained from the court is of great importance, for both people passing through and in terms of the aspect of the surrounding buildings. The court is quite formal yet is not forbidding and has the typical intimate atmosphere of the Temple. However, this is probably due to its enclosed nature (as is the case with the other courts) rather than to its treatment.

Architecturally and aesthetically the court works very well, with little scope for improvement save for strategically placed planters to break up the red-brick walls (Fig. 8.7). The court would have added interest if the floorscape of the lower level was changed, perhaps to cobbles or to a more interesting paved design. The uses of Elm Court are limited and it is suggested that they could be expanded by the provision of seating at the western and north sides that would not dramatically change the nature of the area. The seating would have to be small benches so as not to take up much space as the wide pavements of this court add much to its character. Although the grassed area may appear bare, the trees do provide some cover, without being too dominant, adding pleasant shade to the area and patterning the pavement and surrounding walls.

The Other Courts

Other courts show a variety of landscape styles and uses. Two large courts, King's Bench Walk and Brick Court, are used for car parking for people working within the Temple. King's Bench Walk is extremely busy and has little of the intimate collegiate character of the other courts but at the north eastern corner the

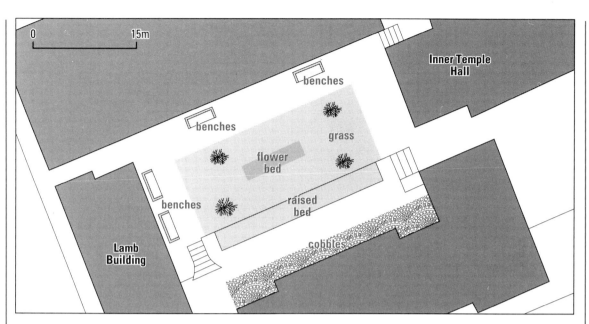

Figure 8.7   Suggested improvements to Elm Court

raised area known as The Terrace provides good views over the Inner Temple garden. The provision of seating on The Terrace would undoubtedly increase its use since it is already used for informal seating at present.

Pump Court is of similar design to Church Court; however, the paved area works better here due to the much smaller scale and the provision of two trees that lend shade and pattern the floorscape. Because of its small size and its walkway characteristics, there is little scope for development or improvement.

However, Hare Court has been sadly neglected and now has characteristics of a wasteland site. This is another court that could be improved by fundamental redesign. It is suggested that it is made into a 'green' court with a large grassed area, perhaps with a central archway feature, with flowerbeds, small trees and shrubs. The paved pathways could be retained and separated from the grassed areas by low railings.

The Inner and Middle Temple gardens, although having no public access, are very important green spaces in this sector of the City. They are of immense aesthetic value, whether viewed from the Inns of Court or from the Victoria Embankment. As there is no

public access, there is no need for developments such as seating and litter bins. However, the green space survey shows that both gardens have a low proportion of saplings in their tree populations; this could cause problems in future years, although they both have many young trees which could bridge the gap between the older ones and those newly planted.

*   *   *   *   *

The main functions of the open spaces of the Inns of Court are as pedestrian walkways, with a secondary role as architectural features. Although privately owned, they are minor tourist attractions generating some visitors to the Temple area. This leads to a conflict in their use; improvements to the area must take into account their private and intimate character. By encouraging greater recreational use (by, for example, the provision of seating) this aspect of their character may be spoiled. Any improvements must not hinder their use as walkways by workers and must be easily maintained as the Inns employ no permanent staff to look after them as a college might have. However, the Inns of Court are a unique area in the City and must be maintained and improved at all costs.

Plate 8.13 Kings Bench Walk

Plate 8.14 Brick Court

Plate 8.15 Pump Court

Plate 8.16 Hare Court

Plate 8.17 Inner Temple

Plate 8.18 Middle Temple

Conclusion

In this chapter we have examined some of the green spaces in three different areas of the City. In the south eastern sector the green spaces are all small and, apart from All-Hallows-by-the-Tower, tucked away among office buildings, some publicly, some privately owned. In the central western sector the spaces examined in this chapter and chapter 4 were larger and with more scope for aesthetic improvement and greater encouragement of use by the public. The south western sector is the greener sector of the City in terms of area but most of the spaces are either closed to the public or so enclosed within the Inns of Court that few find them other than those using them as a regular thoroughfare. Nevertheless these green spaces are an integral part of an aesthetically important whole which forms part of the very fabric of the history of the City of London.

The financial centre

CHAPTER 9

The Evaluation of Open Space

The preceding chapters have highlighted the ways in which trees and open spaces contribute to the environmental quality of the City. In order to justify the retention of present open spaces and to facilitate the planning of new ones, their environmental value needs to be assessed.

The open spaces of the City are, in a sense, 'unused' pieces of land, as they do not contribute directly to the City's primary economic functions. The City depends on a 'built-up' infrastructure for its continued survival as one of the world's major business centres. Open spaces fulfil no economic function as, in most cases, there is no monetary return for their presence. However, they enhance environmental quality by providing areas for relaxation, foils to traffic and buildings, some improvement of atmospheric quality, and 'rural' elements of both scenic diversity and habitat for birds. Open spaces can therefore be perceived as being of great value to the City's working population, as well as being an integral part of the City's fabric.

Placing an actual monetary value on green spaces is especially difficult, due to the problem of ascribing such values to trees, birds and greenscape. Nevertheless these 'non market values' must be taken into account and need to be managed and maintained if they are to remain environmental assets desirable to the City's working population and visitors. There is no logical reason why they should not be 'valued' despite criticisms which can readily be leveled at such attempts. That such 'assessments' are necessary is widely accepted. Economists use the monetary unit, which is the most common and easily understood, to establish easily comparable values. Some approaches to the problem

are outlined below.

Table 9.1   The scheme for the valuation of street trees used by the Arboricultural Association (1984), after Helliwell.

Factor	Points Score			
	1	**2**	**3**	**4**
1 **Size of tree**	small	medium	large	very large
	3-10 m²*	11-50 m²*	51-200 m²*	>201 m²*
2 **Form**	poor	fair	good	especially good
3 **Useful life expectancy**	10-20 years	21-40 years	41-100 years	101+ years
4 **Importance in relation to setting**	barely suitable	fairly suitable	very suitable	especially suitable
5 **Presence of other trees**	many	some	few	none
6 **Special factors**	none	one	two	three
(*e.g.* Historical/botanical interest, siting to obscure an unpleasant view)				
7 **Accessibility to viewing population**	distant	nearby	fairly close	very close

* = height x mean crown diameter

Physical Evaluation

Most Physical Evaluations ascribe point values for measurable characteristics of open spaces and then assign a monetary value to the resulting scores, so giving a measure which enables the value of open spaces to be directly compared with those of other features.

Table 9.2   A scheme for the valuation of street trees modified from the Swiss system see Radd (1974).

Factor

1   Classification figure

Species	Points Score
Acer pseudoplatanus	4
Catalpa sp.	7
Fraxinus excelsior	4
Platanus acerifolia	3
Quercus sp.	9
Robinia pseudoacacia	4
Tilia x europaea	5

2   Aesthetic value, state of health

Solitary, avenue trees – legally protected, historically important	10
Solitary, avenue trees or in groups – important to beauty, healthy and strong	9
Healthy and strong	8
Slightly damaged – accident or pruning	7
Healthy, average growth	6
Healty, average growth, deformed	5
Weak due to habitat – reasonable longevity	4
Weak due to habitat – decaying	3
Weak, damaged – short life span	2

3   Location
(All trees in the City of London are same category)

Town/City centre or protected zone	10

4   Size Index Figure

Trunk circ. (cm)	Points & score index	Trunk circ. (cm)	Points & score index
30	2	140	28
40	2.8	150	30
50	4	160	32
60	5.6	170	34
70	7.6	180	36
80	10	190	38
90	12.8	200	40
100	16	220	42
110	19	240	44
120	22		
130	25		

For comparison with C.L.P. Surveys:

'Saplings' <15 cm;	'young' 16-34 cm;
'mature' 35-180 cm;	'over mature' >181 cm.

Table 9.3   A scheme for the valuation of green and other open spaces adapted from Helliwell (1976).

Factor	Points Score				
	1	**2**	**3**	**4**	**5**
1 **Size (m²)**	1-500	501-1000	1001-2000	2001-5000	>5001
2 **Proximity of users (offices/ shops)**	distant	→→→	→→→	→→→	adjacent
3 **Access**	private - closed	private - limited	public - limited	public - - hr.	public - 24 hr.

Environmental quality

Attributes	Subjective Score 1–5	Mean
a Urban		Rural
b Incongrous		Harmonious
c Noisy		Calm
d Littered		Tidy
e Dull		Attractive

Although there are several methods in use for tree evaluation, two are most relevant for the City; an adaptation of Helliwell's system used by the Arboricultural Association (1984), and the scheme used by the Association of Swiss Parks Administration (Radd 1976). In addition, a method for green space evaluation has been adapted from Helliwell's Small Woodland Evaluation (1976).

The criteria for each evaluation scheme are presented in Tables 9.1-9.3. After survey and scoring, the totals for each criterion are multiplied together to give an 'amenity' score for trees or green space. To convert this to a monetary value, based on the Arboricultural Association recommendation, one unit would be worth £4 (at 1987 prices) this is used here for the two Helliwell schemes. For the Swiss system the amenity score should be divided by 5.91 (£1 = 5.91 Swiss francs in 1974) and multiplied by 4 to take into account inflation to 1987.

Two City streets were surveyed (London Wall and Gresham Street) and the total value of street trees calculated (at 1987 prices) listing the two schemes outlined above (Tables 9.1 and 9.2).

Although these two methods of evaluation share similar environmental factors, differing emphasis and points scores result in different monetary values. Thus the Helliwell system for the evaluation uses 7 criteria with a maximum score of 4 for each one giving a theoretical total maximum of 16,384 points or £65,536 per tree. The Swiss system using only four criteria but with widely variable points scores gives a theoretical maximum of 39,600 points (for trees up to 240 cm trunk circumference) or £26,802.

Table 9.4   The monetary values of street trees in two streets in the City of London derived from use of the schemes outlined in Tables 9.1 (Helliwell) and 9.2 (Swiss).

Street	Helliwell		Swiss	
	total	£/m	total	£/m
London Wall	£201,144	£227.54	£111,769	£126.43
Gresham Street	£36,144	£69.51	£23,478	£45.15

In Table 9.4 London Wall has the greatest value according to both schemes. Using the Helliwell system the value overall and in £ per metre is approximately double that given by the Swiss system. In the case of Gresham Street the Helliwell value is only one and a half times that of the Swiss system. The value differences between the two systems can be explained by the emphasis given to particular features. Architectural, aesthetic considerations and rarity value are emphasised in the Helliwell system while ecological factors are stressed in the Swiss system. Using Helliwell for London Wall most factors score highly with resulting high monetary values but this is less so for Gresham Street. The Swiss system scores somewhat more highly in GreshamStreet relative to the Helliwell system as arboreal factors are more prominent.

The results for evaluating open spaces following Helliwell (1974) are shown in Table 9.5.

As expected, the largest green space in the City, Finsbury Circus, has the highest value (£288,000), although its value per square metre is relatively low, especially when compared to the very small St Alphage Garden, which

Table 9.5   Physical evaluation of selected open spaces using the scheme outlined in Table 9.3

Name	Area (m²)	Value (1987)	£ per m² (1987)
Aldermanbury Square	306	£8,640	28.23
St Dunstan in the East	1482	£86,480	58.29
St Mary Staining	529	£19,440	36.74
Finsbury Circus	7284	£288,000	39.54
Stationers' Court	446	£6,912	15.49
St Alphage Garden	567	£72,000	126.98
Seething Lane	771	£24,576	31.87
Church of Holy Sepulchre, Newgate	591	£24,576	41.58
Paternoster Square	3799	£15,360	4.04

has the very high value of £126.98 per square metre indicating that the size of an area, although of great importance, is not the only factor taken into consideration. The environmental quality of the space is of great importance in this evaluation, accounting for five of the eight criteria. This weighting in favour of environmental quality prevents large open spaces being over valued regardless of their quality. It can be seen from the table that the lowest value per square metre is Paternoster Square, which emphasises the point. Smaller green spaces, although limited in size, may have more to offer users, or have more 'rural' characteristics, and this is directly reflected in the evaluation scheme.

St Alphage Garden, although only the sixth largest site surveyed (567 m²), has the highest value per square metre. It scores highly because of its good access, its proximity to potential users (both Barbican residents and office workers), and its extremely high environmental quality (scoring maximum points on three of the environmental criteria). This contrasts with the nearby Aldermanbury Square which, although two-thirds the size, has less than a quarter of the value of St Alphage Garden. The square has good access and is very close to potential users but it scores very poorly on environmental quality. However, although it is given a relatively low value under this scheme, Aldermanbury Square is a pleasant feature, which lightens the undistinguished buildings which surround it. In spite of its low rating, based on this scheme, the square can be said to fit into its surroundings. If such a factor (as appropriateness) were added to the scheme, Aldermanbury Square would be seen to be more valuable. In contrast, the very large Paternoster Square, which has a low value (£4.04 per square metre) due to its poor environmental quality, merely function as an extension to the harshness of the surrounding buildings.

Stationers' Court provides a good example of how a space may be assigned a very low value because of low scores in only two criteria. Although the environmental quality of the space is high, it is privately owned, closed to the public and is small; the low scores on these factors depress the final value so that it is second lowest in the survey. Because the factors are multiplied together, relatively small differences in scores will be greatly magnified and the final values may show wide differences.

Obviously these schemes demonstrate that physical evaluations have a number of limitations for trying to establish monetary values for trees and open spaces and are open to many criticisms. One of the foremost of which is the open ended structure of the schemes. By adding to the number of factors scored, greater is the potential monetary value as suggested for Aldermanbury Square.

Another criticism is the 'subjectivity' in the choice of factors to be scored within and between systems which may lead to certain areas appearing more favoured than others. On a more positive note however, it can be seen that evaluations based on certain sets of criteria, architectural or ecological for instance, might well be of particular value in certain circumstances in establishing rank orders of value.

If the limitation of these schemes of physical evaluation are recognised and due care is taken in interpreting the results a useful evaluation of the City's trees and spaces is possible. However, the arbitrariness of substituting points scores with 'monetary values', however notional, remains.

Opportunity Cost

Since the City of London depends for its continued existance on office buildings, green spaces are in a sense 'uneconomic' use of land. One way of assessing their notional monetary value is to estimate the potential financial return in terms of rent from developing the site for commercial purposes, in other words the opportunity cost of green space.

There are a number of ways of calculating these 'shadow' values and several assumptions are made concerning the site itself, for instance, location, size, cost of initial purchase, planning permission for development (which would be highly unlikely due to the Corporation of London's policy to resist the loss of existing open space). Finsbury Circus is an ideal site to value in this way. It is the largest greenspace in the City and lies on the fringe of the prime banking and insurance areas. Its residual site value has been calculated in terms of discounted future rents against the cost of development. With office rent levels at £64.84 per m^2 per annum (Hillier and Parker pers. comm. 1988) a notional areal value of £4,704,298 per annum can be estimated for Finsbury Circus. This calculation gives a more realistic 'market' value, some 20 times greater, than that calculated for the physical evaluation. However, similar criticisms can be raised to applying notional market values to green spaces which cannot be valued in traditional market terms, as were raised to applying monetary values in the physical evaluation.

Another aspect of opportunity cost can be expressed as how much a developer is prepared to forgo, in terms of lost rents, by incorporating atria or adjacent open space into a new development. Many new City office blocks such as the Spicer and Regler Building, Latham House and most spectacularly Crosby Court, Bishopsgate, all include atria and/or open space within their design. However, no direct 'foregone' rent value could be extracted for such developments. The plot ratio defines the exact amount of building development allowed by planners (Corporation of London 1986), and the inclusion of an atrium or open space may be used as an incentive for the consent of planning permission; therefore newly created open spaces such as these may not reflect any direct value, but may be just a statutory requirement. Nevertheless atria and adjoining open space developments are important, providing lightwells and adornments to a building that can increase the buildings marketability and even the company's status as it may appear that it can afford an 'uneconomic' use of its floorspace. However both factors are very difficult to measure and to express in monetary terms.

The evaluation of green spaces through measuring the rent forgone by the inclusion of atria has not been successful due to the many different reasons for their inclusion. If atria were included only to increase the environmental quality of the development, the forgone rent could be a useful measure. However, this form of development often occurs simply as a pre-requisite to planning permission being granted

Perceived Value

It can be suggested that the value of green spaces may be reflected in rental premiums paid for offices and residential premises adjacent to, or with a view of, a green space. The Corporation believes that the presence of an attractive working environment is very important to the economic future of the City. Rental variations between offices around Finsbury Circus were studied in order to establish any perceived importance of the green aspect.

According to Allsop and Co., rental premiums for furnished subletting offices in Salisbury House facing Finsbury Circus are generally £2-3 higher than for those facing London Wall. However, this value is not solely attributable to green aspect, for according to Weatherall, Green and Smith, offices facing the green space are generally larger units, so making direct comparisons difficult. It seems more likely that the acquisition of offices by City firms is based more upon availability and centrality for their purposes rather than a 'green' location. However, it is conceivable that environmentally attractive sites add slightly to their marketability.

The pressure for office floorspace in the City has meant that available City offices have been easily marketable due to the prestigious address. Therefore, it would seem that there is no direct link between green aspect and office rent levels. However, the value of green spaces may be more realistically represented in the

prices of residential accommodation with or without a green aspect. Flat prices within the Barbican complex were studied (Barbican Letting Office pers. comm.) to try and determine any differences or patterns in price levels based on 'green aspects'. No difference in rent or rate values were found between flats in Gilbert House (which faces directly onto a green space) and Seddon House, which faces offices in Aldersgate Street. Furthermore, no differences in value were found in the similar flats of Speed House, Andrewes House and Thomas Moore House, even though their green aspects differ. As the major residential development in the City, the Barbican has a high demand for flat purchase, especially by professionals. This may mean that the importance and convenience of a City address in this example overshadows any value that may be associated with green aspect.

More importance is attached to the general outlook of each flat, those in Defoe House being valued £1,000 higher than those in Andrew House despite the fact that the latter adjoins gardens in Fore Street. Valuers have made an allowance of 5% of the value for depth of view, thus flats on higher floors have greater value due to their panoramic views of London. For example, the additional value of a top floor flat in Lauderdale Tower is £65,000 (1987) compared to a similar second floor flat. This suggests that the increased value is ascribed to the view; although this will undoubtedly include a green space element, the actual value of the green space aspect is impossible to extract.

A green aspect, therefore, is not a useful measure of the value of the City's open spaces. It has been shown that land demand is so high in the City that any importance attached to green space value is secondary to the value attached to the prestige of having a City address, both among firms and residents.

Nevertheless 'perceived value' is undoubtedly an important concept in overall terms, as a reflection of the benefits received by the City's population from the use of land for open space. Green spaces may help attract businesses and residents to the City, although their actual value as a factor in attraction is minor, and very hard to determine. However, green spaces are of great importance in making a more pleasant working environment for businesses located in the City. With the current trends of expansion in new technology, businesses are no longer required to be located close to one another, therefore the environmental quality of the City may become more important in determining how many firms stay in the City, and how many will continue to be attracted to it.

As before, the measurement of benefits is a major problem; obviously a green aspect will be perceived as a benfit by most people, but remains elusive to measure monetarily.

Costs and Benefits

Cost-benefit analysis attempts to quantify the advantages and disadvantages of alternative courses of action in terms of a common monetary unit. Here it is used simply to identify and quantify the benefits that accrue from having green space and the costs and constraints which are generated by them. Some parameters commonly employed in cost-benefit analysis of 'valued landscape' are not, however, applicable here, for example, the cost of getting to City green spaces is not relevant. It is possible to employ a very simple form of this method here. The costs are quite tangible (labour costs, cost of plants and other supplies, and premises expenses, etc.), but the benefits are less so.

Using information from the City of London Planning and Communications Committee, the cost and benefits were examined for public open spaces and churchyards sites under the Corporation's control. Taking the revised figures for 1986-87, the tangible costs and benefits can be listed (Table 9.6).

This measure of expenditure relates to all the Corporation controlled open space, that is, public open space (36,794 m²) and churchyards (34,971 m²).

total area of green space	= 71,765 m²
therefore net cost per m²	= £9.47 p.a.

Whilst expenditure rates will vary between the green spaces an average cost can be worked out and applied to specific sites.

Table 9.6   Expenditure on and income derived from public open spaces and churchyard sites controlled by the Corporation of London in 1986-87.

Expenditure (costs)	£
Employees	460,300
Premises-related expenses	108,700
Transport-related expenses	21,600
Supplies and services	139,100
Agency and contracted services	600
Central, departmental and technical costs	69,400
Capital financing costs	78,000
Total expenditure (costs)	**877,700**

Income (benefits)	£
Customer and client receipts	
sales	0
fees and charges	125,100
rental income	15,100
Grants, reimbursements and contributions	
surpluses transferred	0
receipts from other funds	48,800
other contributions, etc.	9,100
Total income (benefits)	**198,100**
Net expenditure (costs)	**£679,600**

Table 9.7   The net benefit of selected green spaces (1986/7).

Site	Benefits (Helliwell)	Costs (£) p.a.	Net Benefit
Aldermanbury Square	£8,640	2,898	£5,742
St Dunstan in the East	£86,400	14,030	£72,370
St Mary Staining	£19,440	5,009	£14,431
Finsbury Circus	£288,000	68,979	£219,021
Stationers' Court	£6,912	4,223	£2,689
St Alphage Garden	£72,000	5,369	£66,631
Seething Lane	£24,576	7,301	£17,275

Obviously if only tangible costs and benefits are considered most, if not all, City open spaces would register a net cost, either to the Corporation of London, as shown in Table 9.6, or to private or corporate owners. However, if benefits can be measured monetarily, and an attempt to do so is set out in Table 9.7, then it can be shown that these sites provide a considerable net benefit. Certainly, as with the previous methods discussed, the figures remain notional but nevertheless should be considered in any overall managed evaluation of these spaces. The method emphasises the very considerable intangible benefits of open spaces to the City.

A Composite Evaluation Scheme for the City's Open Spaces

It is apparent that none of the above methods alone is ideally suited to authoritative evaluation of the City's open spaces. Each method is specific, suited to particular aspects of open space value. In addition, with the exception of some aspects of opportunity cost and the cost and benefit analysis, the values tend to be based on the subjective judgements of the valuer. The wide differences in the values assigned by even the most closely related methods (the Helliwell and Swiss systems) illustrate some of the difficulties involved. By combining some of the methods into a 'composite' scheme, a wider based and more useful evaluation is possible.

The method advocated here modifies the direct land values of open space according to their environmental quality. Land in the City is under constant development pressure. As open spaces generally provide no monetary return, their value can never be as great as that of their value for development. A developer will be willing to pay more than the 'green space value' for development land so as to gain the economic return. This does not happen because of Corporation of London planning controls, therefore the values calculated here are always less than the residual site value (discounted future rents against development costs).

Using office rental values from Hillier and Parker (1988), the residual value of each of seven green spaces was calculated (see Table 9.8). Although the City is a small area, variations do occur – these were taken into account using the 1988 Office Rent Control Map (Hillier and Parker 1988).

By multiplying the residual value by the environmental quality value the hypothetical commercial rent level of the land is related to its use as an open space. As the value will be less than the potential development value of the land, it is realistic in terms of its 'economic' use. The size of the green space is taken into account in the calculations of the residual value; however, access to the space and its proximity to potential users were not measured (although they could be easily included). The highest possible score for environmental quality is 25 (see Design and aesthetic quality index in Table 3.1). The actual score obtained, expressed as a fraction of this, was multiplied by the residual value of the site to give a composite figure. The values calculated for the seven green spaces surveyed are shown in Table 9.8.

The highest value is given to the largest green space, Finsbury Circus, three factors contributing to its value: the area has the highest rent levels in the survey; it has a large area and so has a high residual value; and the high scores for environmental quality ensure that this value is not reduced significantly. The major factor in determining the value is the rent level, followed by environmental quality, as this gives a high composite value per square metre.

Where green spaces have the same rent levels, environmental quality will determine the value of those spaces. When the five green spaces with rents at £484.38 per square metre are compared, it can be seen that the environmental quality value can change the final value substantially – the difference between St Dunstan in the East garden (environmental value 0.76) and St Mary Staining (0.56) is £98 per square metre. St Dunstan's garden is also £89 per square metre higher in composite value than Aldermanbury Square, which has a higher rental value. In effect the high environmental quality of the former increasing its composite value in comparison to Aldermanbury Square.

The composite values differ from site to site, as is to be expected, but the small variation in values per square metre makes the method effective in assessing relative green values given the small variation in rent.

Finally a 'willingness to pay' factor may be added. This is derived from the cost (to the Corporation of Lon-

Table 9.8 The proposed composite evaluation calculated for each of the selected sites

Site	Rent (£ sq. m)	Residual Value	Environmental Quality	Composite Value Total	£/m²
Aldermanbury Square	538.20	£164,689	0.52	£85,638	279
St. Dunstan in the East	484.38	£717,851	0.76	£545,566	368
St. Mary Staining	484.38	£256,237	0.56	£143,492	270
Finsbury Circus	645.84	£4,704,298	0.76	£3,575,266	490
Stationers' Court	484.38	£216,517	0.72	£155,892	348
St. Alphage Garden	484.38	£274,643	0.72	£197,743	348
Seething Lane Garden	484.38	£373,456	0.64	£239,011	310

don) of maintaining open spaces (see Table 9.6).

Table 9.9 The composite value of selected open spaces as modified by the addition of the maintenance costs assumed to be £9.47 per m².

Site	Costs (£)	Modified Value total	£/m²
Aldermanbury Square	2,897	£88,535	289
St Dunstan in the East	14,034	£559,600	378
St Mary Staining	5,009	£148,501	280
Finsbury Circus	68,979	£3,644,245	500
Stationers' Court	4,233	£160,125	359
St Alphage Garden	5,369	£203,112	359
Seething Lane	7,301	£246,312	319

Conclusion

In presenting these evaluation schemes' this chapter has highlighted many of the problems associated with the evaluation of open spaces. No one method can give a value that is not open to criticism. The physical evaluation schemes alone are unsuitable because they take no account of the commercial demand for land in the City, and because of their subjectivity, and in the choice and scoring of criteria. Opportunity cost, although giving a realistic value for the land in development terms, does not provide a measure of the social benefits arising from the green spaces themselves. It was not possible to use perceived value due to the special demand on City land, although it may be of use in other areas (for example, in South London at least £10,000 may be added to the cost of a house facing Clapham Common: this could be interpreted as the perceived value of its 'green-aspect'). Cost benefit is a useful exercise but here again there are problems of assessing benefits due to their intangible nature.

The integration of evaluation schemes provides a way of gaining an overall view of the many elements that contribute to green space value and can be taken as a point of reference providing a framework for evaluation and a basis for further discussion.

CHAPTER 10

Concluding Remarks

Trees and open spaces are important elements in any urban area. In the City they form an integral part of the fabric and in many instances provide a desirable continuity in an environment of seemingly inexorable redevelopment. This survey has attempted to give substance to these assertions, firstly, by providing a data base recording the major characteristics of more than 350 open spaces and nearly 2000 trees. Secondly, by exploring the contribution trees and open spaces make to many aspects of life within the City of London.

The survey includes a brief description of how the present pattern of open spaces evolved. Many, such as those associated with the City's churches have a very long history and the gardening traditions of past centuries are still carried on by the Worshipful Company of Gardeners. However, many of the present City open spaces were created as a result of post war developments such as those to the south and east of St. Paul's and the many green spaces found within the Barbican complex. An interesting example is the creation of a garden

Plate 10.1   Crutched Friars

Plate 10.2   St. Mary's Aldermanbury

(Plate 10.2) in the space left when the bomb damaged church of St. Marys Aldermanbury was removed. After a period of over thirty years the garden has gained a pleasing maturity (Plate 10.3) and has become a far more valuable asset as a result. More recently a number of new open spaces have been created such as those associated with Cutlers Court (Plate 10.6), Crutched Friars (Plate 10.1) and the Broadgate development just outside the City (Plate 10.4).

The considerable variety of open spaces, from small traffic islands to large parks and gardens, from pavement planters to piazzas, has been examined and discussed. The offices of the City, especially new ones (with the notable exception of the Lloyd's building), are often of uniform style thus any type of open space can add diversity to this increasingly monolitic townscape. Open spaces are architectural features in their own right, forming part of the townscape and setting off and complementing the built environment. Conversely, some spaces, such as St Alphage Garden, take much of

their character from the surrounding built environment. This interaction between 'built' and 'natural' environments gives the City much of its present unique character.

The survey has highlighted the considerable importance of open spaces as a recreational resource. Of the various types of open space in the City, perhaps the most important (and certainly the most noticeable) is green space. Hackett (1983) writes 'open plan offices with ample supplies of indoor plants, the urban forest, and the urban farm are surely indications of a policy for city people to be closer to a green landscape'. City green spaces fulfil this need for 'nature' not only in a practical way but also provide a refreshing psychological uplift in a high technology business environment.

Of all the elements of nature present within the City, trees are perhaps of greatest importance, being 'the mainstay of most programmes of environmental improvement' (Gilbertson and Bradshaw 1985). Trees

Plate 10.3   St Mary's Aldermanbury

represent the most striking aspect of the 'green' city. Whether as individual street trees or within open spaces they are important as architectural elements acting as environmental foils to the bulk of buildings, creating the illusion of space in confined areas providing a sequence of colours, patterns on buildings and dappled shade on floorscapes. It can be argued that the City would be incomplete without the richness, texture and diversity provided by its trees. As has been demonstrated, trees and greenery perform another invaluable service in ameliorating various forms of pollution (Corporation of London 1978c).

The various functions of open spaces highlighted in the survey demonstrate their continuing importance to the City environment, therefore it is imperative that the present network should be retained and expanded wherever possible. The future of many spaces, although seemingly assured by the Corporation of London is uncertain, as many spaces (especially private spaces) are under pressure to be redeveloped due to the high

Plate 10.4   Cutlers Court

demand for land in the City. In the past the Corporation of London has recognised that 'with economic difficulties, firms may consider turning recreational areas into more profitable use'. However, Corporation of London policy is to recommend that new open spaces are provided at least equal in size to any areas that are lost through redevelopment wherever possible. Although it is argued that the use of land in this way is uneconomic, the survey has highlighted the benefits of such use, both to the City environment, and from the amenities open space provides. These benefits can justify the costs of the provision and maintenance of open space. The evaluation of open spaces can be carried out successfully using the 'composite evaluation scheme', although the values obtained must be interpreted with care they do emphasise the need for a high priority to be given to open spaces and trees in global budgetary allocations.

*   *   *   *   *

The survey found both public and private open space throughout the City was generally well maintained, attractive and highly appreciated, it also indicated less positive features:

- overall the present picture appears to be one of marking time. Few open spaces have been lost, while equally it appears that within the many new developments in the City such as Ludgate Hill, Little Britain and along the riverside, few open spaces, especially green spaces, are being created.

- The various evaluation indices used in the survey suggest that some open spaces, particularly those lesser known, or those with particular technical, legal or impending development problems, are in need of enhancement. In many cases this could be achieved quite simply and even on a less than permanent basis by hedge and shrub planting to 'contain' spaces (for example the Moorgate Pavements) and screen them from vehicular and pedestrian traffic. This has been effectively achieved at Holborn Circus (see Plates 4.21 & 4.22).

Plate 10.5   Broadgate

- Undoubtably tree planting has increased in recent years but the high number of young trees recorded is partly accounted for by the fact that many in this size category are found in tubs. Further, it does not appear that many trees have been planted specifically to replace the presently mature trees, especially planes, which so characterise the City's landscape. It would seem to make economic sense to plant nearby to succeed as ageing trees cost more to maintain and keep safe.

- Much of the City is deficient of street trees, therefore a vigorous policy of street tree planting should be encouraged. In addition to environmental benefits one or two trees in an otherwise bare street can totally transform the townscape. Despite the costs involved and the well known physical difficulties associated with establishing trees in trafficed streets on balanced benefits outweigh costs.

- A fashionable trend for some business developments in the City has been the creation of atria. These enclosed private green spaces are often very attractive features (Plate 10.6). Nevertheless, from an environmental and recreational point of view open spaces with public access are preferable to atria. Wherever practicable developers should be positively encouraged to incorporate open spaces with public access into their plans.

Plate 10.6   Crosby Court, Shoreditch

- Maintenance problems associated with open spaces and trees beset any urban area. These are of some concern within the City. Bird fouling is unpleasant, a considerable nuisance and a health hazard. It is a problem which is ongoing and costly to deal with. It is particularly common in some of the most used open spaces. There are no easy solutions, it is a matter of control rather than elimination, of continuous cleansing of sites and garden furniture. These services are well maintained by the City and the problem is generally kept to managable proportions. However, people should be discouraged from feeding birds' especially feral pigeons' and leaving waste in gardens and open spaces.

- Another problem is caused by the use of some of the City's less well known and peripheral sites by those not conforming to society's behavioural norms. Their occupation of open spaces particulaly in summer, discourages peoples' use of those open spaces of which the Seething Lane Garden is but one example.

If as a result of these and other problems such as vandalism the standard of open spaces in the City were to be generally perceived as unsatisfactory, then the image of open spaces, especially green spaces, as attractive oases for lunchtime snacks and relaxation would inevitably be diminished and an ambivalence is created in the minds of would be users (see Hayward and Weitzer 1984). Furthermore, should environmental quality be allowed to deteriorate seriously, then their value would be undermined and lead some to see open spaces as a 'disbenefit' to the City.

Some of the problems alluded to here are being tackled by the Corporation of London. However, if their policies on open spaces and related matters (Corporation of London 1986) are to be actively prosecuted, if some of the inequalities in open space provision between the periphery and the core are to be addressed, if new plantings are to be carried out to ensure the tree population remains stable, if street tree plantings are to be encouraged where practicable, if City workers and visitors are to continue benefitting from the presence of gardens in their midst... then a concerted partnership and overall strategy will be necessary between developers, business interests, individual members of the public and the Corporation of London to achieve these objectives.

This survey has gone some way to preparing the ground for the monitoring of resources and the development of an ongoing master programme. It has emphasised the many values attributable to the City's gardens and trees and in so doing has raised the City's green credentials so that those charged with the responsibility for their continuance will not have future cause to lament the demise of a major asset within the City of London.

References

Aldous, T. (ed.) 1979 *Trees and Buildings, Complement or Conflict?* RIBA Publications Ltd. 95 pp.

Arboricultural Association 1984 *An Evaluation Method for Amenity Trees.* Arboricultural Association Leaflet.

Bacon, G.W. *c*1946 *Bacon's large scale plan of the City of London.* G.W. Bacon & Co. Ltd., London and Edinburgh.

Batten, L. A. 1973 *Population dynamics of suburban blackbirds.* Bird study. 20: 251-258.

Beckerson, D. W. 1980 A guide to: plant sensitivity to environmental stress. *Landscape Architecture*, 70 (3).

Benson, J. F. 1981 Animal communities in an urban environment. *Landscape Research,* 6 (3): 8-11.

Bernatsky, A. 1960 *Von der mittelatterlichen Stadtbefestigung zu den Wallgrünflächen von heute.* Ein Beitrag zum Grünflächenproblem deutscher städte, 123pp.

Bernatsky, A. 1975 Les Rôles des arbres dans la ville, pp 79-84. In *L'Ecosystem urbain, application à l'agglomération bruxelloise,* Duvigneaud *et al* (eds). Brussels.

Boardman, B. 1982 The City's secret gardens. *Illustrated London News.* 270: 40-41.

Bradshaw, A. 1971 Derelict Land, Is tidying up going too far? *The Planner.* 3:85-88.

Brown, M. 1983 Design of planting and paved areas and their role in the city, pp87-124. In *City Landscape.* Grove, A.B. and Cresswell, R.W. (eds) 1983. Butterworths. 196 pp.

Burman, P. and Lloyd, D. 1979 Open spaces and landscape. pp 145-150. In *Save the City – a conservation study of the City of London,* Lloyd, D. (ed).Society for the Protection of Ancient Buildings, London.

Carter, H. 1981 *The Study of Urban Geography.* Edward Arnold. 434 pp.

Chandler, T. J. 1962 Diurnal, seasonal and annual changes in the intensity of London's heat-island. *Meteorological Magazine,* 91: 146-153.

Cleary, F. E. 1982 *The Flowering City.* Metropolitan Public Gardens Association.

Collins, M. 1984 *Urban Ecology.* Cambridge University Press.

Coronio, G. and Muret, J., 1976 Typologie des espaces verts. In *Loisirs - Guide pratique des équipments.'* Centre de Recherche d'Urbanisme.

Corporation of London Improvements and Town Planning Committee, 1944. *Report on the preliminary draft proposals for post-war reconstruction in the City of London.* Batsford. 64pp.

Corporation of London, 1946. *Reconstruction in the City of London.* Interim Report to the Improvements and Town Planning Committee by their Joint Consultants. 20pp.

Corporation of London, 1970. *Pedestrian Movement Survey 1969.* (typescript)

Corporation of London, 1976. *City of London Development Plan: Background Study, Tourism.* Corporation of London Department of Architecture & Planning.

Corporation of London, 1978a *City of London Development Plan: Background Study, Archeology.* Corporation of London Department of Architecture and Planning.

Corporation of London, 1978b. *City of London Development Plan: Background Study, Walkways and Pedestrians.* Corporation of London Department of Architecture and Planning.

Corporation of London, 1978c. *City of London Development Plan: Background Study, Recreation and Leisure.* Corporation of London Department of Architecture and Planning.

Corporation of London, 1978d. *City of London Development Plan: Background Study, Architecture.* Corporation of London Department of Architecture and Planning.

Corporation of London, 1979. *City of London Development Plan: Background Study, Environmental Quality.* Corporation of London Department of Architecture and Planning.

Corporation of London, 1984. *City of London Draft Local Plan.* Written statement and proposals map. Corporation of London Department of Architecture and Planning.

Corporation of London, 1986. *City of London Local Plan.* Corporation of London Department of Architecture and Planning.

Cowling, D. C. 1973 *Gleadless Valley: grass survey.* Department of Landscape Architecture, Sheffield University. (typescript)

Cullen, G. 1983 *The Concise Townscape.* Architectural Press. 196 pp.

Denayer-de Smèt, S. 1975 Les Bioindicateurs végétaux. pp 157-173. In *L'Ecosysteme Urbain Application à l'Agglomeration bruxellois.* Duvigneaud, P. and Denayer-de Smèt, S. (eds). Brussels.

Dix, H. M., 1981 *Environmental Pollution: atmosphere, land, water and noise.* Wiley and Son, Chichester 286pp.

Douglas, I. 1983 *The urban environment.* Edward Arnold, London 229pp.

Duvigneaud, P. 1974 L'Ecosystème "Urbs" *Mém Soc. Roy. de Botanique de Belgique*, Brussels. 6: 5-35.

Duvigneaud, P. 1975 Introduction a la connaissance de l'écosystème urbain. pp 16-33. In *L'Ecosystème urbain application à l'agglomération bruxellois*, Duvigneaud and Denayer-de Smèt, S. (eds). Brussels.

Duvigneaud, P. and Denayer-de Smèt, S. (eds) *L'Ecosystème urbain application à l'agglomération bruxellois.* Brussels

Emery, M. 1986 *Promoting Nature in Cities and Towns: a practical guide by the Ecological Parks Trust.* Croom Helm, London. 396pp.

Fairbrother, N., 1974 *The Nature of Landscape Design.* Architectural Press.

Fiebig, D. M., 1982 *Survey of Inner London squares.* Unpublished project report, City of London Polytechnic.

Fisher, J. K. 1976 *City of London, Past and Present.* Oxford Illustrated Press. 62 pp.

Forshaw, J. H. and Abercrombie, P. 1943 *County of London Plan,* prepared for the London County Council. Macmillan, London. 188pp.

Fowler, D. and Cape, J. N. 1982 Air pollutants in agriculture and horticulture. In *Effects of Gaseous Air Pollution in Agriculture and Horticulture*, Unsworth, M.H. and Ormrod, D. P. (eds). Butterworths. 532 pp.

France, R. 1979. Guildhall–Cheapside–Barbican pp. 48-55. In *Save the City – a conservation study of the City of London*, Lloyd, D. (ed). Society for the Protection of Ancient Buildings, London.

Freeman, J. 1979 Conservation in the City 15-20. In *Save the City – a conservation study of the City of London*, Lloyd, D. (ed). Society for the Protection of Ancient Buildings, London.

Fruin, J. J. 1971. Designing for pedestrians – a level-of-service concept. *Highway Research Record* 355. Highway Research Board.

Furcolow, M. L., Tosh, F. E. 1961. The emerging pattern of urban histoplasmosis. *New England J. Medicine,* 264: 1226-1230.

Gilbert, O. L., 1981. Plant communities in an urban environment. *Landscape Research*, 6 (3): 5-7.

Gilbertson, P. and Bradshaw, A. D. 1985 Tree Survival in Cities: the extent and nature of the problem. *Arboricultural Association Journal,* 9: 131-142.

Gill, D. and Bennet, P. 1973. *Nature in the urban landscape: a study of city ecosystems.* York Press.

Goode, D., 1983. The Gunnersbury Triangle, a new precedent for nature conservation. *London Environmental Bulletin.* 1 (2): 7-8.

G.L.C. 1983 *'Thirty years on' – a review of air pollution in London.* A discussion paper. Greater London Council. 42pp.

Greater London Council, 1985 *Nature conservation guidelines for London.* Ecology Handbook No. 3. Greater London Council.

Greater London Ecology Unit, 1986 *A nature conservation strategy for London: woodland, wasteland, the tidal Thames and two London Boroughs.* Ecology Handbook No. 4. Greater London Council.

Hackett, B. 1983 Opportunities in City landscape pp 1-9. In *City Landscape,* Grove, A.B. and Cresswell, R.W.

(eds). Butterworths. 196 pp.

Helliwell, D. R. 1967 The amenity value of trees and woodlands. *Arboricultural Association Journal,* 1, 128-131.

Hayward, D. G. and Weitzer, W. H. 1984 The public's image of urban parks: past amenity, present ambivalence, uncertain future. *Urban Ecology* 8: 243-268.

Helliwell, D. R. 1976 Small Woodland Evaluation. (mimeo)

Hillier and Parker 1988 Office Rent Control Map.

Isles, J. (ed), 1987 *Owl Prowl.* London Wildlife Trust, London.

Johnson, M.S., 1978 Land reclamation and the botanical significance of some former mining and manufacturing sites in Britain. *Environmental Conservation,* 5 (3): 223-228.

Laxen, D. and Schwar, M. 1985, *'Acid Rain' and London.* Greater London Council. 31pp.

Lloyd, D. 1979 (ed) *Save the City – a conservation study of the City of London,* Society for the Protection of Ancient Buildings, London.

Majerus, P. and Denayer-de Smèt, S. 1974 L'Analyse Foliaire de métaux lourds en tant qu'Indicateur de pollution urbaine. *Mém. Soc. Roy. Bot. Belg.* 6: 71-84.

Manning, O. 1979 Designing for nature in Cities pp 3-36. In *Nature in Cities,* Laurie. I.C. (ed). Wiley and Sons, N.Y.

McKenzie, A. 1869 *The Parks, Open Spaces and Throughfares of London.*

Mickleburgh, S. 1985 Bats in London. *Wild London,* 18.

Montier, D. 1977 *Atlas of breeding birds of the London area.* Batsford. 288pp.

Murdock, W. T., Travis, R. E. *et al* 1962 Acute pulmonary histoplasmosis after exposure to soil contaminated by starling excreta. *Journal of the American Medical Association,* 179: 73-5.

Newsam, M. D. 1988 *An investigation of lead levels in trees within the City of London.* Unpublished project report, City of London Polytechnic.

O'Connor, F. B. 1981 Wildlife in the City. *Landscape Research* 6 (3): 2-4.

Ogilby, J. 1676 *Survey of the City.*

Owen, D. 1978 The natural history of Britain and Northern Europe. *Towns and Gardens.* George Rainbird Ltd, London. 224pp.

Pitt, D., Soergill, K. and Zube, E. 1979 in *Nature in Cities,* Laurie, I. C. (ed). Wiley and Sons.

Pushkarev, B. S. and Zupan, J. M. 1975 *Urban Space for pedestrians: a report of the Regional Plan Association.* MIT Press.

Radd, A. 1976 Trees in towns and their evaluation. *Arboricultural Journal,* 3,1.

Richards, N. A. 1983 Diversity and stability in a street tree population. *Urban Ecology,* 7: 159-171.

Southwood, T. R. E. 1961 The number of species of insect associated with various trees. *Journal of Animal Ecology,* 30: 1-8.

Spellerberg, I. 1981 *Ecological Evaluation for Conservation.* Edward Arnold. 59 pp.

Steubing, L. 1975 Les Dommages causés aux plantations par la pollution atmospherique et filtration des poussieres par la vegetation pp 147-156. In *L'Ecosystème urbain application à l'agglomération bruxelloise*, P. Duvigneaud and Denaeyer-de Smét, S. (eds). Brussels.

Tandy, C. 1972 *Handbook of Urban Landscape.* Architectural Press. 175 pp.

Tansley, A. G. 1939 *The British Islands and their Vegetation.* Cambridge University Press.

Teagle, W. G. 1981 The water's edge. *Landscape Research.* 6 (3): 25-27.

Thearle, R.J.P. 1968 Urban bird problems. pp 181-197. In Murton, R. K. and Wright, E. N. (eds) 1968 *The Problem of Birds as Pests.* 17 Symp. Inst. of Biology. London, Academic Press.

Tomlinson, M. J., Driscoll, R. and Burland, 1978 Foundations for low-rise buildings. *BRE Current Paper,* 61/78.

Transport and Environment Studies (TEST), 1985 *The Accessible City, a report by TEST for the Campaign to improve London's Transport.*

Tregay, R. 1984 In search of greener towns. *Planning Outlook.* 27 (2): 59-62.

Van Rooden, F.C. 1983 Greenspace in cities pp 10-24. In *City Landscape*, Grove, A.B. and Cresswell, R.W. (eds). Butterworths. 196 pp.

Wang Chia Hsi, 1982 Recent research on relationships between air pollution and plants in China. p472. In Unsworth, M.H. and Ormrod, D. P. (eds) *Effects of Gaseous Air Pollution in Agriculture and Horticulture.* Butterworths. 532 pp.

Weinreb, B. and Hibbert, C. (eds) 1983 *The London Encyclopaedia.* Macmillan, London. 1029 pp.

White, J. T. 1984 *Country London.* Routledge & Kegan Paul.

Wroth, W. W. 1896 *The London Pleasure Gardens of the 18th Century.*

Youngman, P. 1979 The landscape of central areas pp 123-129. In *Quality in Urban Planning and Design,* Cresswell, R. (ed). Newnes Butterworths.

Appendix

Location Map

Species	2	3	4	Map Square 5	6	7/8	9	10	11
Abies sp.							1		8
Acacia sp.									
Acer negundo				1		1	2	4	1
Acer pseudoplatanus		5			5		1		6
Acer sp.		3	1	16	3	4	3	8	12
Aesculus hippocastanum	20			5					3
Ailanthus altissima		2	1	2	2		3	1	6
Alnus glutinosa								1	
Alnus incana				1					
Araucaria araucana									
Arbutus unedo									
Betula sp.	20		1	3		3	5	4	16
Carpinus betulus								6	
Catalpa bignonoides			2	2				11	2
Cedrus sp.									
Cercis siliquastrum				1					2
Chamaecyparis lawsoniana				1			3	4	
Cotoneaster frigidus									
Crataegus sp.	4	1			1	2	4	1	
Cryptomeria japonica									
Davidia involucrata									1
Embothrium coccineum lanceolatum									
Eucalyptus sp.									
Fagus sylvatica			1	3			1	4	18
Ficus carica			2	1				5	2
Fraxinus excelsior	23	7	3	7	3	4	6	15	2
Ginkgo biloba				3					2
Ilex aquifolium									
Juglans regia									
Laburnum sp.							2		1
Larix sp.								1	4
Laurus nobilis									
Liquidambar styraciflua									1
Liriodendron tulipiferae				2			2		
Magnolia sp.				2					19
Malus sp.				1			2	1	
Metasequoia gluptostroboides								2	2
Morus nigra		1			1			1	8
Paulownia imperialis									
Platanus acerifolia		28	20	11	28	20	19	31	54
Populus balsamifera				3					
Populus nigra								2	2
Prunus persica			1						
Prunus sp.	20	3	1	4	3	5	8	17	39
Pterocarya fraxinifolia			2						
Quercus robur		1		4	1			3	12
Quercus rubra			1						
Rhus typhina laciniata					2			1	
Robinia pseudoacacia		2	3	2					6
Sambucus nigra									
Salix alba				12			1		3
Salix pentanora				6					4
Salix x sepuleralis 'chrysocoma'				7				2	
Sophora japonica		1			1				
Sorbus aria				2					5
Sorbus aucuparia								3	8
Sorbus hybrida			1						1
Sorbus vilmorinii									
Stewartia pseudo-camellia		1			1				
Stranvaesia davidiana							2		
Taxodium distichum								4	4
Taxus baccata			2						2
Tilia x europaea		2	1		2		1	11	36
Tilia platyphyllos		2		8	2			6	24
Tilia tomentosa							1	3	
Ulmus glabra pendula		1			1			2	4
Ulmus vegeta		2	1	2	2				4
Ulmus wheatleyi									7
Palm						1		1	6
Cypress									20
TOTAL NUMBER OF TREES	87	62	44	114	62	38	58	132	338

Map Square

Species	12	13	14/20	15	16	17	18	19
Abies sp.					30	11	3	12
Acacia sp.								
Acer negundo	1						6	
Acer pseudoplatanus	1		3		3		2	2
Acer sp.	2	1	5		5	1	4	8
Aesculus hippocastanum		1	2	3		1	1	1
Ailanthus altissima						1		1
Alnus glutinosa								
Alnus incana								
Araucaria araucana					1			
Arbutus unedo								1
Betula sp.	5	17	6	3		5	3	12
Carpinus betulus					2	2		1
Catalpa bignonoides	2			4	1	1	1	
Cedrus sp.								
Cercis siliquastrum				1				
Chamaecyparis lawsoniana								
Cotoneaster frigidus			11					
Crataegus sp.		14		7			1	5
Cryptomeria japonica				2				
Davidia involucrata				1				8
Embothrium coccineum lanceolatum								1
Eucalyptus sp.		1						
Fagus sylvatica	2		3			11	1	9
Ficus carica	2			2				1
Fraxinus excelsior	2	1			5	1	3	3
Ginkgo biloba	2			1	2			4
Ilex aquifolium		12		2			8	7
Juglans regia				2		1		1
Laburnum sp.				6		4		1
Larix sp.					3			
Laurus nobilis		8						
Liquidambar styraciflua								
Liriodendron tulipiferae		1		2				
Magnolia sp.		1		9		4		6
Malus sp.	7			9		4	1	1
Metasequoia gluptostroboides				1				
Morus nigra		1		1				3
Paulownia imperialis								
Platanus acerifolia	26	29	39	79	9	2	6	47
Populus balsamifera								
Populus nigra							5	
Prunus persica				1				
Prunus sp.	7	9	1	10	14	10	3	11
Pterocarya fraxinifolia								
Quercus robur	1	1			2			6
Quercus rubra								1
Rhus typhina laciniata								2
Robinia pseudoacacia	4		2		2	8	1	10
Sambucus nigra							1	
Salix alba	6	4	2			13	2	4
Salix peutandra								
Salix x sepuleralis 'chrysocoma'	1		2					1
Sophora japonica								
Sorbus aria	1	12	2	2	2		14	11
Sorbus aucuparia			10	1				
Sorbus hybrida			2	1				
Sorbus vilmorinii								
Stewartia pseudo-camellia								
Stranvaesia davidiana								1
Taxodium distichum								
Taxus baccata								
Tilia x europaea	2	41	5				2	6
Tilia platyphyllos	4		3				1	7
Tilia tomentosa				1				
Ulmus glabra pendula								
Ulmus vegeta					2			6
Ulmus wheatleyi					5			
Palm								
Cypress								
TOTAL NUMBER OF TREES	85	154	98	151	88	76	71	201

Index

Surveys
    birds   99
    City trees   89
    City wide   17, 19
    method   90, 99
    methods   17
    Open Space   18
    open space use   55
    Pedestrian Movement Survey 1969   18
    results   20

T

Temperature   79, 116
Temple Gardens   57, 118, 119
Tennis   55
Tourism   61
Tower Hamlets,
    London Borough of   25, 27, 29, 57, 90
Tower Hill   121
Tower of London   57, 61
Tower Place   122
Townscape   31, 53
Traffic   42, 65, 81, 114, 117
Traffic Islands   51
Tree Record File   18, 90
Trees   32, 89
    age   90, 93
    architectural role   32, 35, 36, 39
    causes of loss   96
    density   91
    diseases   96
    distribution   91
    management   96, 97, 106
    numbers   29, 90
    planting   70, 96, 129
    pollution   96, 111
    size   90
    species   88, 90, 95, 98, 118
    street trees   36

    visual impact   36
    water demand   95
Tudor period   6, 7
Turnagain Lane   128

U

Urban habitats   83
Urban-Rural Index   39, 41
User Surveys   55, 127

V

Vacant land   29, 85, 109
Vagrants   60, 80, 128
Valuation
    of street trees   143
Vandalism   96
Vedast Place   72
Vegetation   32
    and area   87
    and rurality   87
    diversity   86, 88
    for wildlife   86
    of space   87
    structure   21
    unsown   85, 86

W

Walbrook   36
Walking trails   61, 79
Wallside   65, 76
West End   28, 29, 90
Westminster, City of   14, 28
Wildlife   83, 98, 106
    public attitudes   109
Winchester Corner   68
Worshipful Company of Gardeners   70
Worshipful Company of Plaisterers   73